The
SUSSEX
Weather
Book

In recent years, the weather has wreaked havoc in Sussex. Blizzards, floods, tornadoes, landslides, mudslides, tidal surges, thunder, lightning, hurricane-force winds, sunshine and drought have arrived in towns and villages like villainous heroes. The reason for such extremes, say the pundits, is global warming. It may well be true, but wasn't it said that the wet weather during the 1914-18 war was caused by the firing of guns from Flanders which triggered off sensational rainfall ? Were not radio waves, nuclear bomb tests, space satellites and even Concorde individually blamed for creating atmospheric pollution that changed the weather in the 1930's, 40's, 50's and 60's ? It is a fact that the weather in Sussex has always been immensely variable. In this unique pictorial record of the county's most dramatic events we have some of the evidence.

Bob Ogley, Ian Currie and Mark Davison

Froglets Publications and Frosted Earth
A Joint Publication

Froglets Publications Limited,
Brasted Chart, Westerham,
Kent. TN16 1LY.

© 1995

Bob Ogley, Ian Currie and Mark Davison

ISBN: 1 872337 13 9

Cover Illustrations:

Front Cover: Boys cycling in floods January 1994, by George Godden

Back Cover: The Pontoon Bridge over the A27 January 1994, by George Godden

This book was originated by Froglets Publications of Brasted Chart and Printed and bound by Staples Printers Rochester Ltd.

Jacket design: Alison Clarke

First impression: November 1991,
Reprinted December 1991, June 1995

A special thank you to Fern who helped with the research and was greatly involved with the production at all stages

ACKNOWLEDGEMENTS

IN the summer of 1991, through local newspapers in East and West Sussex, we appealed for reminiscences about the dramatic meteorological events that have occurred in a county, well-known for a great variety in its weather. We also spoke on *Radio Sussex* about our proposed book and invited its listeners to send photographs of those blizzards, floods and storms which are now part of Sussex folklore. In each case, the response was fantastic. From East Grinstead to West Wittering, from Battle to Bosham came anecdotes, newspaper clippings and, in many cases, a photograph. Forgotten historic moments came to light in dusty Sussex attics and cellars and we are indebted to all those who responded so enthusiastically.

We would like to thank the staff of libraries and museums who have provided considerable help in our research, editors and photographers of local newspapers and local history enthusiasts who have given valued advice. Foremost on this list is the Evening Argus who provided a treasure chest of photographic memorabilia.

Special thanks also go to the following: Mr Spike Milligan, Sussex Archaeological Society, The Climatological Observers Link, The Royal Meteorological Society, Edward Reeves of Lewes, Dennis Rogers of Seaford Museum, Hastings Museum, Bexhill Museum, County Records Offices at Lewes and Chichester, Brighton Museum, Mr. Jon Wynne-Tyson, Mr. Peter Jerrome of Petworth Society, Mr. Richard Tollett of Rye Harbour RNLI, Mr. Peter Bailey of Newhaven Maritime Museum, Mr. Martin Hayes and staff of Worthing Library, Mr John Rogers, Mr Charles Kay, Sir Norman and Lady Longley, Mr E.Milne-Redhead, Miss Jane Scott, Mrs Nell Brown, Mrs Sarah Page, Mr and Mrs M. Gillen, Mr Michael Goldsmith, Mr John Hurren, Mr Stuart Douglas and and all the people who contacted us with offers of help. We are particularly indebted to Mr Brian Girling for allowing us access to his wonderful postcard collection.

PHOTOGRAPH CREDITS

The photographs and prints in this book were kindly supplied by the following: **Evening Argus, Brighton:** pages 79, 110, 113, 115, 120, 121, 122, 124, 125, 127, 128, 129, 130, 132, 133, 135, 137, 138 (top), 139 (bottom), 140, 148, 149, 150, 151, 153, 154, 157, 158, 161, 168. **West Sussex Library:** pages 25, 29, 139 (top). **East Sussex Library:** pages 14, 30, 31, 68. **Sussex Archaeological Society:** pages 7, 9, 16, 17, 19, 23, 27. 99. **Bexhill Museum:** 20, 26 (bottom), 64, 105. **Hastings Museum:** 26 (top), 67, 74. **Steyning Museum:** 35. **Mr Peter Brandon:** 25, 78 (bottom). **Sussex Express:** 131. **Hastings and St. Leonards Observer (Michael Martin):** 123, 163, 136, 138 (bottom), 141. **P.C. Glen Matthews:** 159. **Beckett Newspapers:** 70, 71, 101, 105, 155 (bottom), 163. **Mid Sussex County Times:** 111, 113, 116, 118, 157. **Portsmouth Publishing:** 109, 116, 117. **John Topham Picture Library:** 80, 83, 84, 85, 89, 90, 107, 119. **Midhurst and Petworth Observer:** 103. **TVS:** 158. **Commander H.J.Brooks:** 142. **National Trust:** 143. **West Sussex Gazette:** 169. **East Grinstead Observer:** 162, 146 (top and bottom). **Rye Art Gallery:** 36. **Lillian Rogers:** 37, 38. **Mrs G.F.Buss:** 43, 78 (top). **Mr Jon Wynne-Tyson:** 48, 49, 50, 83. **John Rogers:** 90 (top and bottom). **Kent County Library:** 58 (bottom). **Garland Collection (Peter Jerrome):** 59, 61. **Garland Collection (West Sussex County Records Office):** 64, 82. **East Grinstead Museum:** 66. **National River Authority:** 70, 98. **Seaford Museum:** 73, 75. **Mrs E.M.Wynter:** 77. **Mr and Mrs Macdonald-Smith:** 86. **Chichester Observer:** 86 (bottom), 109. **Eric Nash:** 88. **Charles Seager:** 91. **West Sussex County Times:** 93. **Roger Baker:** 109 (top). **Edward Reeves:** 96, 97. **Dulcie Parkhurst:** 100. **Mr and Mrs Bagnall-Oakeley:** 103. **Newhaven Local Maritime Museum:** 104. **Philip James:** 112. **B. Cal. News:** 118. **Andrews, Kent and Stone:** 147. **George Godden:** 167, 170, 171, 172. **Vic Cook:** 168. **John Elms:** 172.

The Sussex Counties

WEST SUSSEX

Gatwick Airport
Crawley
East Grinstead
Weir Wood Reservoir
Horsham
Ardingly Reservoir
WEST SUSSEX
Billingshurst
Petworth
Haywards Heath
Midhurst
Pulborough
Burgess Hill
R Adur
R Arun
SOUTH DOWNS
Steyning
Arundel
Chichester
Littlehampton
Worthing
Bognor Regis
Selsey

R Medway
Bewl Reservoir
Wadhurst
Ashdown Forest
Crowborough
Mayfield
R Rother
Darwell Reservoir
R Tillingham
Uckfield
Heathfield
Rye
R Brede
EAST SUSSEX
Battle
R Ouse
Winchelsea
Hailsham
Lewes
Arlington Reservoir
Hastings
SOUTH DOWNS
Bexhill
Hove
R Cuckmere
Polegate
Pevensey
Brighton
Newhaven
Eastbourne
Seaford
Beachy Head

EAST SUSSEX

Maps of East and West Sussex, showing the towns and rivers and the great expanse of countryside that these wonderful counties enjoy. In using this map as a guide to the stories and photographs that follow, it must be remembered that in the early decades covered by this book, there was more "traffic" on the rivers than the roads, where turnpikes, as well as great snowfalls, often interrupted the flow. On the farms there were oxen, labourers wore smocks, croquet was played in crinolines, windmills and tidemills abounded and cricket, with two stumps, was played on the village green. The mail coach ran regularly from London to Rye and the London, Brighton and South Coast Railway was in its heyday. On the coast, every town had a pier and, in the country villages, the girls danced round the maypole. A man without a hat was seldom seen. Not every aspect of Sussex life has changed. For the labourers in smocks, the passengers on the railway, the cricketers on the green, the girls on the maypole and the men in hats, there was, as now, a perpetual topic of conversation.....the weather.

Introduction

Sunny Sussex by the sea

"WHEN the Island's seen above the line, Brighthelmstone loses weather fine", goes an old Sussex saying. It means that if the Isle of Wight is plainly visible from the hills behind Brighton, then the next day is sure to be cold and wet.

Worthing, too, has its weather signs. All you have to do is cock an eye up towards Chanctonbury and if you see nothing but mist, then it will soon be raining. "Old Mother Goring's got her hat on. And we shall have some rain".

In Eastbourne, the weather watchers look towards Beachy Head. The masses of chalk which stick out so prominently are called Charleses. From time to time they have an angry, threatening look. "When the Charleses wear a cap, the clouds weep".

The fishermen of Hastings also have a distinctive bad weather sign - a raking sound made by the sea in the bay of St. Leonards. The noise is known as the "bells of Bulverhythe" and when they "ring" a storm is approaching from the west.

We wonder whether the Hastings fishermen heard the bells in the early hours of Friday 16th October, 1987 when that "hurricane" was coming up the Channel on its way to devastate Sussex and change the face of its landscape ? Were the Charleses wearing their caps on 25th January, 1990 when the coastal towns were hit below the belt by a storm that, according to the law of averages, should not have arrived until 2237 ? And was Mother Goring wearing her hat on Boxing Day, 1962 when it snowed so hard that green grass was not seen again until early March ? We guess she was..

Sussex has experienced a long and desperate association with the wind and the waves. Although the climate is mostly benign, it can suddenly change as it did on 14th November, 1875 when Seaford was inundated on a Sunday morning, and hundreds of families fled in terror.

Inland the county experiences a whole range of extreme conditions. The South Downs are notorious for their heavy snow. Many people will recall the blizzards of 1927 and 1947 and the intense cold of 1940 when sheep were frozen by their wool to gorse bushes.

In the valleys, rivers have frequently burst their banks and flooded famland, villages and towns. The great Sussex rivers are the Arun, the Adur, the Ouse, the Cuckmere and the Rother. Often they have sent wild waves lapping down High Streets, through shops and homes, bringing all the usual chaos and heartbreak. Each flood in turn has been described as "the worst in living memory" but the three to take pride of place in Sussex folklore are the floods of 1910, 1960 and 1968.

There have been tornadoes, whirlwinds, dust-devils, earthquakes and such phenomena as hailstones, the size of golf balls and dust from the Saraha which turned the county yellow. There have been landslides, mudslides, fog and smog and, at the other extreme, long, hot summers when temperatures soared into the nineties. rivers and reservoirs ran dry and garden hoses were banned. Who remembers the summer of 1976 when we were advised to take a bath with a friend !

Sussex countryfolk can judge the weather by the way the animals behave. When a cat "sleeps on her brains" and cattle sit down in the fields, when rabbits are seen in the middle of the morning, or sheep stand with their tails to the wind, then rain is on the way.

Rain in Sussex.? It's the sunniest county in England and Eastbourne is the sunniest town. Have a nice day..

CONTENTS

CHAPTER ONE

1066 - and all that

From William's war with the wind and the tempests that helped to reshape the coastline of Sussex to the blizzards and storms of the eighteenth century, here are some of the county's more remarkable weather events. They include a tornado of amazing ferocity, earthquakes, droughts and even a mirage. In terms of meteorological importance they are dwarfed by the greatest battle of all - man's unceasing conflict with the sea.

Easter, 1066: A monstrous light appeared in the sky, silently moving with a tail of fire. Sussex people gazed at it in fright. Learned monks said it was a star called "cometa". Modern astronomers say it was Halley's Comet. It was seen at the time as an omen of doom, a heavenly sign of wrath and fire on earth.

26th September, 1066: Duke William of Normandy and his vast army landed near Pevensey Bay after a long battle with the wind and the waves. The Conqueror had been waiting in the Bay of Seine for the right sailing weather but there was not a breath of a southerly wind for more than a month, extraordinary weather that no sailor in those seas could believe.

It suddenly changed on the 12th September and William cast off for his journey across the Channel. As he did so the wind veered to the west and began to blow with hurricane force. It was the very thing that everyone dreaded. Ships were wrecked on the shore or lost at sea. Many of the Duke's soldiers deserted. The wind backed to the north and the invasion was on the brink of failure.

The southerly wind that William had prayed for came on the night of 26th September. He landed at Pevensey, only to discover there was no army to greet him. Harold Goodwin was engaged with the Norsemen at Stamford Bridge. The Duke met no resistance until the King's battle-weary, footsore army arrived a few days later. The outcome changed the tide of English history.

1205: A great frost began on St Hilary's Day, then 14th January, and continued until 25th March.

1570 : A sudden incursion of the sea at Rye. "Water rose eight or more feet in men's houses at midnight."

February 1578: The sea, in a storm, broke through the beach bank at Bishopstone and formed what is now called the Old Harbour. This was in use until the New Haven was made as a safer exit.

17th February, 1638: A parhelia, or mock sun, seen on either side of the sun, giving the impression of three suns.

16th June, 1663: Withyham Church burnt to the ground in a tempest of thunder and lightning.

3rd January, 1726: King George I, returning from Hanover, was driven into Rye Bay by a "great storm". He walked to Rye and "was very much fatigued". The storm was followed by a heavy fall of snow which prevented the King from proceeding to London. While he was in Rye the mayoress gave birth to a son and the King agreed to be Godfather. The boy was called George.

3rd June, 1747: A very violent thunderstorm washed away a bridge at Midhurst.

29th January, 1748: Multitudes of sheep were lost under snow on the South Downs.

1st November, 1755: The shock from the Lisbon earthquake was felt in Sussex. Water in ponds was thrown several feet above banks. Fish were left on dry land at Midhurst.

23rd November, 1755: A windmill in the parish of Durrington was set on fire by lightning.

8th October, 1765: A ball of fire was seen about 9 o'clock in Chichester. "It was the bigness of a man's head and was, for a moment, very luminous".

4th August, 1777: Lightning killed three people in a field near Falmer.

June, 1791: " Snow on the downs at midsummer."

FAMINE CAUSED BY THREE-YEAR DROUGHT

ACCORDING to the writings of The Venerable Bede, the early Christian historian, there was drought and famine in the province of Sussex that lasted three years and "caused perpetual damnation and an inexpressible calamity of temporal death". So bad was the famine that very often "forty or fifty men would go together to some precipice, or to the seashore and there, hand in hand, perish by the fall or be swallowed up by the waves".

In 681, Bishop Wilfrid came to preach in the province and urged them to get food by fishing "for their sea and rivers abounded in fish". The men gathered eel nets everywhere, cast them into the sea and "by the blessing of God took three hundred fishes".

On the day that Sussex received this baptism of faith "there fell a soft but plentiful rain".   *Taken from Bede's Early History of England, translated by J.A.Giles.*

Last days of Old Winchelsea

1st October, 1250

OLD Winchelsea was once a low, flat island in the south-east corner of Sussex inhabited by wealthy Barons, fishermen and many pirates. Buffetted by gales which blew so frequently, it was known by many as "cold wind island" - an inhospitable place but one which enjoyed considerable prosperity, particularly during the reign of King John. It was a place of rendezvous for the fleets of England and, as a senior Cinque Port, benefitted from toll-free privileges.

At one time Old Winchelsea had 700 householders, 50 inns and 39 squares, or quarters. It enjoyed greater importance than Rye because it was accustomed to a flourishing trade and to the passage of kings. Its decline began on 1st October, 1250 when a devastating tempest hit the little island.

The Elizabethan chronicler, Holinshed, described this most momentous event in the history of Old Winchelsea. "On the first day of October, the moon upon her change, appearing exceeding red and swelled began to show tokens of the great tempest of wind that followed, which was so huge and mightie, both by land and sea, that the like had not been lightlie knowne, and seldome, or rather never, heard of by men then alive. The sea, forced contrarie to its natural course flowed twice without ebbing, yielding such a rooring that the same was heard (not without great wonder) a far distance from the shore. Moreover the same sea appeared in the dark of the night to burne as if it had been on fire, and the waves to strive and fight together after a marvellous sort, so that the mariners could not devise how to save their ships. At Hert-burne three tall ships perished without recoverie, besides other smaller vessels. At Winchelsey, besides other hurt that was done, in

bridges, milles, breakes and banks, there were three hundred houses and some churches drowned with the high rising of the water course."

There were many who believed that Divine retribution was being exacted for the sins of Old Winchelsea. Certainly the little island received stern punishment, not only from the elements but, subsequently, from the sword of justice, for piracy was rife. Ships, whether foreign or English, were being captured, crews flung overboard without mercy and the booty shared. For centuries afterwards, when Winchelsea ships entered western ports, a hatchet was held up to them, as a sign that their ancestors' crimes had not been forgotten.

Prince Edward, later Edward I, made Old Winchelsea pay for the misdeeds. In 1266 he put to the sword all the principal inhabitants involved in piratical enterprises. He then planned and superintended the foundation of a new town on a green hill. It was a wise move. In 1287 the "tempest of all tempests" roared up the Channel. What remained of Old Winchelsea was utterly destroyed. In fact the island and its beaches were washed away leaving no trace. The size and weight of the waves smashed down sea walls, swept away wooden buildings and scoured away the foundations of sand and shingle on which the town was built. Thanks to King Edward the town was, by now, uninhabited.

The exact site of the once-thriving island port is now difficult to discover. A writer in 1724 said "the ruins thereof now lie under the waves three miles within the high sea". Others believe that the lost town is now dry land due to the shifting coastline, but no-one can point with any precision to the site of what was Old Winchelsea seven centuries ago.

Rye rises above its harbour

WHEN the people of Romney dragged themselves from their houses and looked around at the appalling havoc caused by the tempest of 1287, they discovered to their horror that the River Rother had changed its course. The river bed was choked with shingle, sand and debris and all around was the wreckage of ships, inns, houses and churches. The bodies of men were strewn over the shore for many miles.

Where was the River Rother ? It had straightened its course and was flowing almost directly from Appledore to Rye, where the Tillingham and Brede also reached the sea. In triple measure Rye was to benefit and Romney, now without a port, was to suffer.

Over the centuries the land slowly silted up, the Brede all but disappeared, Winchelsea was left stranded and only Rye remained. Then, in 1572, there was another storm. This one drove so violently inland that the sea broke into the low-lying land behind Rye town and the harbour was enlarged. The inhabitants spent thousands of pounds on their new harbour but shingle was continually thrown up and an enormous bar grew across the mouth of "New Harbour".

Within 15 years it was abandoned. Today, Rye is left high and dry and its cliffs rise above dry land. The harbour is a mile downstream with the mouth half a mile beyond that. The superb engraving by William Daniell of Rye town during a high spring tide, rising from its dramatic site above the sea, shows how this medieval seaport must have looked before it was ravaged by the Sussex storms.

Brighton's battle with the sea

1703 - 1756

"BRIGHTHELMSTONE is a poor old fishing town build on the very edge of the sea. The sea is very unkind and has by its continual encroachments, so gained upon them, that a little time more they might reasinable expect it would eat up the whole of the town."

So wrote Daniel Defoe in 1722 when Brighton was desperate to raise enough money to build banks against the tidal surges which came with such frequency. "The expense will be eight thousand pounds", wrote Defoe, "which if we look on the town, would seem to be more than all the houses in it are worth".

Defoe was right. Brighton was disappearing into the sea. In Roman times the distance from the present day front to the edge of the sea was more than a mile but it was slowly and consistently being gobbled up. Between 1292 and 1340 a further 40 acres were lost and by 1665 "a large piece of Brighthelmstone had been submerged including 22 houses and shops and three cottages with three parcels of land attached".

At the start of the Stuart era the population was about 3,000 and the town was "the most flourishing in the county with no fewer than 600 families engaged in fishing". In 1699 a vicious storm took toll of several more acres but it was the Great Storm of 1703, arguably the worst in history, which caused so much damage and misery in Sussex and particularly in Brighton.

The wind began to blow at midnight on 27th November and raged continuously for eight hours. As far as records for those days could be made it was estimated that 8,000 people in Britain perished. At the height of the storm the first Eddystone lighthouse was washed away. When it subsided the people of Brighton found that 101 houses and shops in the lower town had been destroyed by the wind and then devoured by the sea. The upper town also suffered. Two mills were destroyed and the church roof was blown off.

The fisherfolk who survived had not only lost their homes but many of their menfolk as well. Nine men and Richard Kitchener, master of The Cromley were lost. Five of the crew and a young boy managed to get ashore. The Elizabeth was lost with the crew. Only one of the crew of The Happy Entrance was saved. Walter Street had clung to a mast for three days. The Richard and Benjamin went down near Chichester but George Glover, the master and most of the crew saved themselves in the shrouds.

After the storm, Daniel Defoe made a tour of England. This is what he said of Brighton. "Brighthelmstone being an old-built and poor, though poplous, town was miserably torn to pieces and made the very picture of desolation that it look't as if an enemy had sack't it".

The few houses left standing in the town were patched up and the poor folk moved back, but two years later on 11th August, 1705 a south-westerly blew in and destroyed the lower town. There was now no sign of the houses; they were buried beneath a great bank of shingle hurled up by the force of the waves.

By the year 1713 the sea was eating into the cliff which protected the upper town. The cliff was then as far back as the pavement in front of the present day houses of Grand Junction Road and Kings Road, and it crumbled away with every rough sea. In 1713 the sea also flooded the bottom of East Street and into the turning of what is now the Cannon Cinema into the Pool.

The inhabitants of Brighthelmstone called a meeting. They decided that the only answer was a series of groynes and a new sea wall, but where was the money to come from? The people were far too poor. In the end it was decided to apply for a Brief - a fund to help those in distress, when a collection was taken in every church and chapel in the country on a certain day.

Brighton's turn came in 1722 when the charitable collections throughout the land amounted to £1,700 "in order to preserve such of the said towne as was then remaining". It fell far short of the £8,000 required but enabled the authorities to make a start.

It was Dr Richard Russell who eventually saved Brighton. In 1756 he came to the town to effect his marvellous cure for glandular trouble and other diseases by drinking warm sea water and bathing in the sea. During this time a brisk trade was done in salt water "took off the main ocean at Brighthelmstone" and barrels of it were sent regularly to London. With Russell came the nobility. Brighton became fashionable. Money poured in. Sea defences were built and the old ones repaired.

Brighton was winning its long battle with the wind and the waves.

Pool Valley, Brighton was once a small inlet in the foreshore which provided easy access to the River Steine. Today it is pedestrianised and still the area of natural drainage when the sea misbehaves. The print shows the scene during the great Brighton inundation of 17th July, 1850 when the sea came swirling into Pool Valley and clearly caught everyone by surprise. There have been many other notable occasions at The Pool, particularly in 1795 when flooding reached a depth of seven feet, and on 24th November, 1824 during the "birthday storm" which caused so much damage to the Chain Pier.

REMARKABLE MIRAGE AT HASTINGS

A superior mirage is an image seen above the real object. It is caused by light bending downwards when travelling through cold dense air on its way to the eye. Such a refraction was seen by William Latham of Hastings in July 1797, who wrote:

"I was sitting in my house when my attention was excited by a number of people running to the seaside. I was informed that the coast of France was plainly to be seen without a telescope. I went down to the shore and I could see the cliffs on the opposite coast 50 miles distant and from this elevation not to be discerned even with the best glasses."

Mr Latham spoke to sailors and fishermen who were able to point out places they had visited on the coast of Picardy. His letter continued: "Having indulged my curiosity upon the shore for nearly an hour I went to the eastern cliff and a most beautiful scene presented itself to my view. By telescope the French fishing boats were plainly to be seen at anchor. This curious phenomenon continued in the highest splendour till past 8 o'clock."

Such an example of atmospherical refraction had never before been witnessed by any of the older inhabitants, nor by any of the numerous visitors attending, that day, the annual Rock Fair.

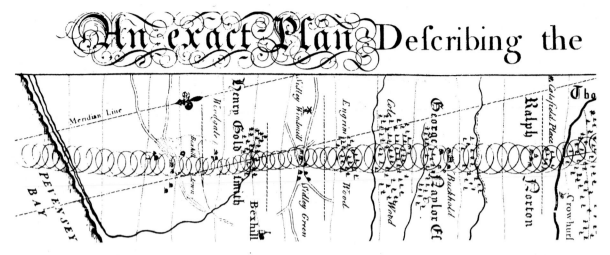

An exact plan describing the

Tornado's trail of terror

20th May, 1729

THE weather was clear and serene in East Sussex. The lanes and downs were bathed in sunshine and only a slight scented breeze disturbed a perfect May day. It was not to last. Suddenly the weather became warmer and by the morning of 20th May it was "exceedingly hot and sultry". A storm was brewing in the Channel.

In the afternoon thick, rolling clouds were "dancing over the sea" off the coast of Bexhill. "At Battel" they looked like "prodigious smoak rolling from a lime kiln". At Ewhurst a strong light was observed from the centre of the blackness, which covered the "face of the Heavens". Lightning began "darting and breaking forth like liquid fire" and the inhabitants were overcome by fear and terror. A tornado was approaching fast.

It came ashore about nine o'clock in the evening and dissipated 20 minutes later at Newingden-Level. The way of the tornado was from south by west to north by east in a direct line over a distance of some 12 miles. The first serious damage was to a house on the lower side of Bexhill Down. The east end of its roof was ripped off and a chimney destroyed. A barn was uplifted and its remains deposited nearly 400 yards away. A "hovel" (makeshift house) was picked up and set down with its thatch barely disturbed.

The tornado moved on to Sidley Green where the force of the wind moved a complete house with its outbuildings a full two inches. About 150 oak trees were "torn out of their roots and shaken to pieces".

Farmhouses and barns were badly damaged. At Loose Farm, near Battle, a large tree was carried over a hedge, and an orchard was destroyed. A hopgarden gate was found a quarter of a mile from where it took off.

The tornado struck with extraordinary swiftness for, in each area, the ferocity lasted only two to three minutes. The trail of damage continued through Sedlescombe and Ewhurst Green, across the Rother towards Tenterden, soon to exhaust itself leaving adjacent areas unscathed. At Colliers Green a child was carried in his chair and set in the fireplace and two dungcarts outside the house were carried away never to be seen again.

1776: Lewes suffered a heavy snowfall on St Hilary's Day in January. A flock of sheep at Ringmer was buried several feet deep but dug out the following day. A flock kept by Mr Martin of Newhaven was buried for 13 days before a dog sniffed them out.

1795: "Such an inundation at Brighton on 26th January as was never before witnessed. It happened between one and two o'clock in the morning and was accompanied by a sudden thaw which succeeded a frost of one month's continuance. The rain melted the snow and water ran in torrents from the circumjacent hills and completely deluged the Lower Castle Square, the Pool and the Steine, to a depth of several feet."

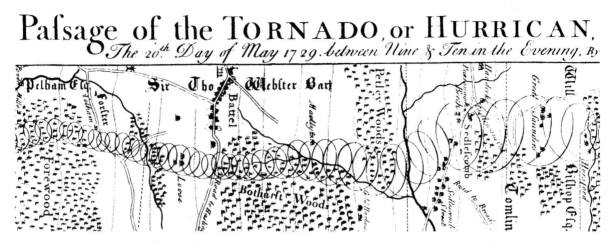

passage of the tornado or hurricane from ....

Blasting of Seaford Head

19th September, 1850

THE damaging effect of Channel storms at the moment of high spring tides and the vulnerability of its low and yielding cliffs has helped to reshape the coastline of Sussex. Headlands have been trimmed back and harbour entrances deflected eastwards by longshore drifting of eroded material. The sea has encroached on land throughout history and erosion has been responsible for the coastline retreat averaging, in some places, between one and two miles since the Roman period.

Nowhere is this more apparent than at Seaford, whose importance has waxed and waned with the changes in the course of the River Ouse and the advance and retreat of the sea.

Whether the Ouse mouth was diverted from Seaford to Newhaven by a violent storm in the sixteenth century, or by a deliberate act of man to improve its navigation, the outfall of the river was repeatedly being blocked by shingle, and in the 17th century the river broke through at a point between Seaford and Newhaven.

Seaford's fortunes did not revive until the arrival of its first seaside patrons and it continued to be plagued by great storms. In the "hurricane" of 1703 the sea overtopped the defences and flowed up to the church gate. In another tidal inflow in 1800, "two ladies was took out of their chamber windows with their maid and set down in a boat".

Desperate efforts were made to prevent encroachment of the sea but none was so drastic as that planned in the mid-19th century when it was decided to blow a large part of Seaford Head into the sea by blasting down a mass of chalk so as to form a groyne which, it was hoped, would prevent the shingle being carried out of the bay.

The blasting, on 19th September, 1850 attracted much attention. There were excursion trains to Seaford and a gunboat took visitors near to the site. It is estimated that 15,000 were present when the mines were fired. It was a complete failure. **Page 23.**

POWERFUL HORSE COULD NOT RESIST THE WIND

THE Sussex Weekly Advertiser on 2nd November, 1795 reported that "it thunder'd, it lighten'd, it hail'd and it rain'd with a degree of violence that is not often exceeded in the most tempestuous months of summer. On one day the wind was so mighty that even the strength of a powerful horse could not resist it, for as a clergyman was riding near Heighton, the violence of the gale took the beast off his legs and forced him down. The rider, much hurt, was obliged to be conveyed home in a post chaise.

At 7 o'clock on Saturday morning, the garden wall of Mr Osborn of Poynings was blown down by the high wind and unfortunately just as a poor woman named Marshall was passing. She was buried in the ruins and dug out with her back broken. She survived only a few hours and then expired in great agony."

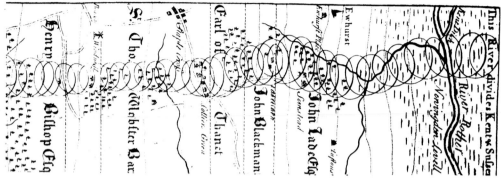

From the Seaside in Sussex, to Newingden Levell.

the seaside in Sussex to Newingden Level

EARTHQUAKES IN SUSSEX

End of the world was nigh !

HISTORIANS studying the incidence of major earthquakes in Britain from archival sources have discovered that great tremors have struck on many occasions and most of them have their epicentre in East Sussex, Kent or Essex. In the third and seventh centuries earthquakes caused substantial loss of life and in the 11th century there were three, all graphically described in the *Anglo Saxon Chronicle*.

The first great tremor, however, was in 1158. which caused 30 casualties in East Sussex and three in West Sussex. There was considerable damage to buildings, including Lewes Castle. In 1247, 11 churches in East Sussex were "reduced to rubble" with at least 50 casualties. In 1382, the Bell Tower of Canterbury Cathedral was "shook down" with further damage in Sussex.

One of the county's best known earthquakes came on the 6th April, 1580 when the great bell in Chichester Cathedral "strake itselfe against ye hammer with shaking as divers clockes and bells in the city and elsewhere did the like". This tremor was immortalised in Shakespeare's *Romeo and Juliet*. "Tis since the quake now eleven years", one of the characters declared. In Kent and Sussex churches were damaged and, according to an old chronicler "the sea foamed and ships tottered. There was heard from the south west a marvellouse greate noyse,

as in the twingling of an eye the same noyse was as though yt had been round about the hearers, and therwith began a most feirce and terrible earthquake". In London two people were killed; they were the first identified victims of a British earthquake.

In 1750 there was a succession of earthquakes over three months which led many people in Sussex to give all they had to the poor in the belief that the "End of the World and the Last Judgement were nigh". All caused major damage with loss of life in East Sussex.

The "Great English Earthquake of 1884" measured 4.9 on the Richter Scale. Shock waves which travelled through Kent and Sussex caused great alarm. The epicentre was in Essex where 1,200 houses were damaged and a child was killed.

Dr Andrew Allen, writing in *Sussex Life* believes that an earthquake as big as any that has hit Italy or Japan could occur in Sussex tomorrow - despite the widespread delusion that the British Isles are free from such horrors. "Given the long-term instability of the seismic zone which runs through Belgium, Holland, Kent , Essex and East Sussex, it is statistically possible that one will occur comparable to any in the past. Without a great deal of seismological research there is no way of knowing whether it will be tomorrow, or in 300 years time."

The only survivor of HMS Brazen is hoisted to safety

Rescued by a cage on the cliffs

THROUGHOUT the centuries thousands of fine ships have been destroyed by the gales which blow so frequently and so violently off the Sussex coast. The graveyard is an extensive one. All the way along the exposed shoreline from Rye to Selsey, bodies and wrecks have been washed ashore and cargo has littered the beaches. Each community has a tale to tell of tragedy, heroism and even miracles.

Among those which have earned a place in folklore is the story of the warship *HMS Brazen*, first seen a few hundred yards out to sea below the cliffs at Newhaven on 26th January, 1800. The ship, which had been captured from the French two years earlier, had run into a south-west gale and the majority of the 106 crew were drowned.

High on the cliffs above the foaming waves were two swinging cranes from which were suspended large cages, designed to hoist shipwrecked mariners to safety. These were the Royal Humane Society's life-saving engines - but they could not reach any sailor until he drifted to the foot of the cliff. In the water the ship was going down rapidly with some men still hanging on. Others were in the sea, clutching pieces of improvised liferafts.

Civilians, operating the cranes, were unable to help. Several sailors nearly made it to safety, only to be engulfed by the sea as they clambered onto the rocks. One man was clinging to a gunslide as he neared the foot of the cliffs. The cranesmen reeled their crane in, wheeled their engine along the cliff edge and let it down again with two men inside the cage. With enormous effort they grabbed the half-sensible sailor, pulled him into the cage and were reeled back to the top of the cliff. Jeremiah Hill, a non-swimmer, was the only survivor.

Next day when the weather was calmer, the bodies could be seen strewn along the strand line from the wreck to the harbour. Wagons from Newhaven came to take them away and they were buried in nearby churchyards. Ten men were never recovered.

A subscription was raised in Brighton to reward the sterling work of the cagemen who operated their crane on top of the cliffs so bravely.

High drama on Sussex seas

IT WAS on the 7th December, 1809, in another howling storm, that seven ships came aground in Seaford Bay. Rocked by the waves which swept over them, many were broken in two and others severely damaged. Townsfolk, awakened by cannonfire in the middle of the night, rushed to the beach and looked on helplessly as passengers and crew from the stricken vessels attempted to swim ashore.

One can imagine those dark hours with sleet, spray and a biting wind through which could be heard the cries of drowning men. Dragoon officers rushed to the beach and, linking arm to arm, formed a human chain out to sea. Although the waves engulfed the leading men, they reached many struggling sailors and hauled them back to shore. In the very midst of the battle between life and death, looters worked unscrupulously in the dark

The onshore storm which followed and an exceptional high tide left many broken hulks on the beach. They were auctioned 12 days later and, on 24th January, the insurers knocked down the stores and equipment that had drifted ashore.

The gallant crew of the Eastbourne Lifeboat, The William and Mary after their heroic efforts in rescuing the crew of the New Brunswick on 25th November, 1883

ON THE 25th November, 1883 the 480-ton barque, *New Brunswick* found herself being blown in towards the cliffs between Beachy Head and Birling Gap in a monstrous gale. The captain dropped anchor, hoisted distress signals and his men lashed themselves to masts as huge waves broke over the ship.

A lightship saw their predicament and signalled the coastguard who telegraphed for the Eastbourne lifeboat. It was five miles from the lifeboathouse to the wreck, too far in such a gale. They would have to launch the boat at Birling Gap.

The people of Eastbourne rallied to help and hauled the *William and Mary* on her carriage through the town. The Anchor Hotel lent six horses and the party drove south-west, climbed a 500-foot hill and crossed ploughed fields. Two and a half hours after leaving the boathouse they arrived at Birling Gap and laid a path with timber to the sea. In torrential rain the crew rowed through the breakers into the teeth of the gale. To the watchers ashore the *William and Mary* could be seen surmounting the crest of the waves and then disappearing as she fell into the succeeding troughs. Waves filled the boat with water but it was drained immediately by the crew.

The lifeboat reached the *New Brunswick* and one by one the men leapt into the sea and were plucked out of the water. The lifeboat returned and the beachparty helped to drag it out of the water, up the slope and into the carriage. The rescue operation alone had taken five hours.

CHAPTER TWO

The Nineteenth Century

A century dominated by many fearsome storms at sea and, on land, some remarkable blizzards. The Lewes Avalanche on Christmas Eve, 1836 was an unprecedented event in the history of England. Eight people died when many tons of snow tumbled from the South Downs onto a row of cottages. There were more great blizzards towards the end of the century involving loss of life. The Brighton Chain Pier was attacked by the weather on so many occasions that its final destruction was almost inevitable.

12th November, 1806: A heavy snow-storm in which Neville, a well-known inhabitant of Brighton was lost in a snow-drift near the spot where the Adur Inn now stands.

22nd October, 1807: A dreadful hurricane. Three brigs, two colliers and a vessel laden with corn were wrecked in front of Brighton town.

30th November, 1811: Earthquake shocks felt at Chichester, Petworth, Arundel and on the coast from Selsey to Shoreham.

January, 1814: Severe cold spell. Below freezing almost incessantly between 3rd and 25th January.

November, 1815: A dozen men from a government cutter were drowned near the site of the Queen's Hotel, Hastings.

29th July, 1816: A waterspout appeared near Arundel in "a most terrific form, descending from a congregated cloud as a dense pillar and working as a spiral screw in a vertical direction".

16th August, 1819: A whirlwind at Hardham with thunder and lightning which entirely swept away a field of barley carrying it higher than trees, which were covered by it.

30th July, 1820: Heavy thunder with large hail-stones. At Portslade and adjoining villages, thousands of linnets, sparrows and small birds were killed by lightning.

29th November, 1836: Windows in Lewes were covered with an incrustation of salt, resembling hoar frost. This was blown in by the great Brighton storm which partially destroyed the Chain Pier.

March, 1839: A few days before the 30th a Will-o'-the-wisp was seen at Chichester. The people of Fishbourne Turnpike Gate said it "came from the marsh towards them until it became extinct in a meadow, 100 yards away".

20th January, 1838: According to Horsham diarist Henry Burstow, the temperature dropped to an unofficial reading of -16F (-26.7C) and gin froze solid. Ice crystals were said to have floated in the air and glistened like prisms when the sun shone on them. Another big freeze-up occurred in 1855.

29th November, 1861: A new system of storm warnings was instigated in Hastings to operate from the flagstaff of the Customs House. The Drum meant stormy winds; the Cone, gale force winds; the Cone and Drum, dangerous winds.

Mid-January, 1866: Severe storms caused great damage to Hastings sea wall. On 11th February the wind blew a "hurricane" all day and many chimney pots were blown off.

Mid-July, 1868: Three months' drought broken by "tremendous thunderstorms in East Sussex".

25th December, 1870: A white Christmas. Scores of people enjoyed skating at St. Andrew's garden, Bulverhythe.

11th July, 1888: Snow fell at Rusper on this day. It was described as the year without a summer.

27th November, 1890: During the first three weeks of November it was unusually mild but an intense surge of cold led to the unprecedented reading of only 14F (-10C) at 4 pm on the 27th. Snow was a foot deep in the Ashdown Forest and caused evergreen trees to bend in all directions.

April 28th, 1895: This was the start of a drought that lasted for 81 days, until 17th July. At Crowborough, only 0.68 inches (17mm) of rain fell during this period. Dry weather continued into 1896 and, by the end of May, represented a loss of water of 1,340 tons per acre.

11th February, 1899: *The Arno*, a steamship sank 4.5 miles from the entrance to Chichester Harbour. Six crewmen out of 18 died.

The Suspension Chain Pier, which was opened on 25th November, 1823, and was one of the magnificent attractions of Regency Brighton.

Nature unkind to churches

THE mellow sandstone churches that stand so prominently and so prettily in dozens of Sussex hamlets and villages have endured, and in most cases withstood, whirlwinds, tornadoes and great gales of hurricane-force. Thunder has boomed around them and they have all been majestically silhouetted by flashes of lightning. Mother Nature, however, has not been kind to all her churches and a few have shown their vulnerability.

The earliest record of a church being set on fire by lightning was in 1621 when the parish church of Mayfield was badly damaged. Just over 40 years later, Withyham Church was "burnt to the ground in a tempest of thunder and lightning" and in another great storm, on 8th August, 1774, the spire of Berwick Church was "consumed by fire". Horsham's turn to suffer came on 23rd November, 1790 when the shingles of the parish church were set ablaze by lightning. They were quickly extinguished - by torrential rain !

Earthquakes have taken toll of many Sussex churches, as described on page 12, but only one case of whirlwind damage is known and that was this century. On 4th July, 1946 a whirlwind

THE SEAFORD SHAGS

There were hundreds of shipwrecks off Seaford in the 15th and 16th centuries caused, not by storms, but the unlawful inhabitants, who altered navigation lights on shore and lit bonfires to confuse ships' lookouts. After ships had foundered on the rocks, rich cargoes were washed up and plundered by the scavenging Seafordians who were frequently compared with sea shags and cormorants by terrified sailors. "Oh God. Protect us from the Seaford Shags", goes an old ship's prayer.

visited the village of Fairlight, near Hastings and caused great damage around the church, high on the hilltop.

More recently, the hurricane-force winds of 16th October, 1987 toppled the spires of St. Luke's United Reformed Church at St Leonard's and St Deny's, Rotherfield. Gravestones were lifted at Crowborough and Hartfield and trees fell onto churches at Ditchling and Uckfield.

At great cost, all have been repaired.

15th October, 1833. Lightning strikes the Brighton Chain Pier.

Stormy days for Chain Pier

ONE of the great sights of nineteenth century Brighton was the Suspension Chain Pier, built in 1823 from the highly original design of Captain Samuel Brown at a cost of £27,000. The grand opening on 25th November was attended by 250 people of "rank and respectability" who heard the speeches and marvelled at the technological capabilities of modern engineers. As they were eating a magnificent lunch and enjoying all the razmataz associated with a historic occasion they would not have known that Brighton's "greatest enemy" would soon be pitting all its strength against this engineering phenonemon.

On 24th November, 1824, the day before the infant pier's first birthday, a storm of "interminable violence" hit Sussex and the sea overtopped the still-inadequate defences. Coastal towns, including Seaford and Brighton, were inundated and the Chain Pier badly damaged. However, it was soon repaired and once again admired by those who came to Brighton in search of health and pleasure.

There was nothing pleasurable about the storm of 15th October, 1833 when lightning "partially destroyed" the Chain Pier, or the "memorable tempest" of 29th November, 1836 which buckled the chains, shattered the platform and caused other damage to a structure now showing signs of weakness.

It is a credit to the early nineteenth century engineers that the Chain Pier actually survived three such violent storms and it was with some relief that many peaceful weather years followed. However, 72 years after the Pier was opened, the weather again showed its malevolent hand. On 4th December, 1896 the "greatest tempest of all" gathered in the sea off Brighton and, on this occasion, battered the pier to pieces.

See pages 30 and 31.

Lewes avalanche kills eight

24th December, 1836

A DISASTER unprecedented in the history of England occurred on Christmas Eve, 1836 when an avalanche fell from the edge of the Downs on to South Street, Lewes, sweeping away a number of cottages known as Boulder's Row. Fifteen people were buried under many tons of snow and eight lost their lives. The tragedy came less than a month after hurricane force winds had ravaged much of East Sussex and it left the town of Lewes in a state of great shock.

The Sussex Weekly Advertiser described the event in graphic detail. "Scarcely has the excitement caused by the effect of the late tremendous hurricane subsided when it becomes our duty to record another, and in its results, a still more calamitous visitation. On the morning of Saturday 22nd December, a heavy fall of snow commenced and continued with scarcely any intermission until Monday. A strong gale swept the snow into drifts of incredible depths so that all traces of roads were lost and communication between towns was prevented by huge barriers of solid snow.

"It was observed on Monday that the violence of the gale had deposited a continuous ridge of snow along the brow of that abrupt and almost perpendicular height, which is based by South Street and the Eastbourne Road, where tons upon tons seemed to hang in a delicately turned wreath as lightsome as a feather but which, in fact, bowed down by its own weight, threatened destruction to everything beneath.

"Considerable fears were entertained on Monday for the line of cottages known as Boulder's Row and these apprehensions were not diminished when a considerable fall occurred at Mr Wille's timber yard which destroyed a sawing shed. Mr Wille advised his neighbours to quit without delay but they refused. At about a quarter past ten two men implored the inmates to lose not a moment if they wished to save their own lives. The poor creatures appeared, however, to be bewildered and could not be prevailed upon to depart. One man endeavoured to drag two women out by force but he was compelled to desist in order to save his own life.

"The snow toppled on the brink and sliding down the steep with tremendous force threw down and completely buried the seven end houses. A gentleman who witnessed the fall described it as a scene of the most awful grandeur. The mass appeared to him to strike the houses first at the base, heaving them upwards, and then breaking over them like a gigantic wave to dash them bodily into the road; and

when the mist of snow, which had enveloped the spot, cleared, not a vestige of habitation was to be seen. There was nothing but an enormous mound of pure white.

"The scene which ensued was heart-rending. Children were screaming for their parents and women were rushing through the streets with frantic gestures in search of their offspring; while in the midst of all this consternation men were hastening from all quarters for the purpose of extricating the sufferers."

The newspaper explained how the first to be dug out was a boy named Jeremiah Rooke. He was alive. A woman was then found quite dead but her body had shielded her child who was found alive. Four more were found dead and then to "a hearty and simultaneous burst from the spectators" three children were discovered alive and uninjured. An old man was found lying across the fireplace. Groaning was heard from the back of where the cottages had been and here a lad was buried several feet deep. The rescuers released a hand and an arm but were obliged to run for their lives as another tremendous heap of snow slipped from its resting place and again buried the lad.

The men, nothing daunted, worked far into the day clearing the snow. One man was buried for six hours. He had received severe injuries and was in a state of extreme exhaustion but not insensible. He asked eagerly for some beer. Late in the evening the last person, a poor girl, was pulled out.

Fifteen people were buried in the ruins and six were pulled out alive. At the inquest the jury returned a verdict of "accidental death" but recorded their admiration for the "intrepid and persevering exertions of those who placed themselves in the greatest peril to save the lives of their fellow creatures".

The Snowdrop Inn, which stands on the site of the cottages buried by snow.

A painting of The Avalanche, which hangs in the Anne of Cleves Museum in Lewes.

The Avalanche

From the Sussex Weekly Advertiser of January, 1837

The snow-storm came on a Christmas night,
And it pil'd its flakes on the cliff's broad height;
And there it lay in its fleecy pride,
When the cold sun gleam'd on the mountain's side.
And the cottagers dwelling beneath the hill,
Reckless of danger, regardless of ill
Busied themselves in domestic care,
Mother and daughter and child were there.
The old man close to the fireside stood,
To quicken the course of his torpid blood;
And the budding infant, with its glances sweet,
Gambol'd and crew at the old man's feet.
At length came a sudden rushing sound,
And the avalanche made its fatal bound;
It dealt destruction to all beneath,
And whelm'd the inmates in darkness and death.
Sad and loud was the funeral wail
That was borne abroad on the biting gale;
They gather'd the victims no pow'r could save,
And buried them all in one common grave.
The snow is melted, the storm is past,
And hush'd is the voice of the wintry blast;
Lightly and mild will the summer breeze blow,
And the dead be forgotten who slept in the snow.

In the nineteenth century it was not uncommon to find sharks basking off the south coast. In 1813 five were clearly seen on one day from Brighton. The engraving (above) shows a Squalus Maximus, or basking shark which was caught off Brighton on 3rd November, 1812. The photograph below shows a group of civic dignitories looking at the carcass of a whale, which was washed ashore at Pevensey Bay in the storm of 16th November, 1864. This became a sightseers' attraction.

Eastbourne Pier, opened in 1872, destroyed in 1877 was then rebuilt a few feet higher.

Eastbourne Pier has gone !

1st January, 1877

HUNDREDS of people gathered on the parade at Eastbourne on the evening of New Year's Day, 1877 in order to have a front-seat view of a storm that "would test the town's great pride and joy, the Eastbourne Pier, to the utmost". The Pier had been open for five years, and had withstood some mighty seas but this gale, blowing south west by west, looked "particularly mischievous". While many people barricaded their doors and windows, others actually walked on to the pier itself. This is how the event was described by the *Eastbourne Herald*.

"Looking out sea-ward, the scene presented was grandly wild, but at the same time gloomy and portentous; huge waves were seen rolling in, their white crests raised towards heaven, whilst the wind scattered the spray far and wide, forming a dense mist on the scene. It was a quarter past eleven. Huge crowds began to assemble and the sea continued to rise and advance with slow but steady step towards our shores; the waves increased in size, breaking like mighty giants on the doomed pier and along the whole length of the parade.

"The scene was magnificent in the extreme, quite baffling description; the waters rose up like an enormous wall, looking fearful in their power and descended with a blow which can only be compared to Vulcan's Hammer. The Pier began to stagger and violently oscillate and it became evident that it had completely broken in the centre. The excitement was now intense, as the first half, which was the

weakest and received the greatest fury of the waves gradually sank over to the east.

"A few trusting and venturesome individuals believed it could yet resist the mighty power of the ocean, for they kept their places upon it. Old Neptune still raged, and boiled, and foamed with greater madness when, at a few minutes past twelve, a terrible crash was heard - a thrill of horror passed through the crowd - the Pier was gone. At first it was thought the men on the Pier had gone with it. But they saved their lives as if by a miracle, scrambling on to the falling floor by clinging to the railings, and being pulled upon terra firma by those at the entrance".

The *Sussex Daily News* said that the waves rose so grandly and so stupendously that at the inland town of Hailsham, seven miles distant - and, in fact, for miles beyond that, they could be observed, dashing and curling on the shingle of Pevensey Bay. After the storm had abated, the Pier could be seen lying flat on the sands while the bottom half stood out of the water like an island. Marine Parade had the appearance of a perfect wreck and fishermen's huts were completely knocked down.

"At this point", said the *Eastbourne Herald*, a foolhardy man, named Hatton, nearly lost his life through greed of gain. He kept rushing into the sea to pick up pieces of lead pipe but on one occasion he was tumbled over by the waves and washed out to sea. Gallant fellows risked their lives to save him".

They ran for their lives

14th November, 1875

IT was Sunday morning in Seaford. Many people were making their way to church for the morning service and others were in their homes wondering when the wind, which had been gusting for three or four days, would leave them in peace. It changed to hurricane force and just before high tide on this infamous day the sea broke over the beach and forced its way into the town centre. So sudden was the assault that scores of people abandoned their homes and fled. Those in church heard the commotion, took one look at the mountainous waves and ran for their lives.

Within 30 minutes waves were lapping against houses and shops. A wooden ship on the beach was battered to pieces and baulks of timber washed into the town, causing great damage to homes in Steyne Road. The water came up to the Bay Hotel and down the High Street to Mark Wynter's chemist shop. Seaford was evacuated. Some went to Corsica Hall and others to Hardwick House. One bedridden old man who lived in Church Street was rescued from his bedroom window by boat.

Writing about the flood in *Old Seaford*, the photographer, R.W. Wynter relates: "The sight in front of the town was beyond description. Bathing machines, boats, tables, chairs, beds and miscellaneous items were floating about in all directions. Many curious incidents occurred. The wheel from a bathing machine was forced partly through a window in Marine Terrace. A haystack in Lyons Place was carried away by the tide and stranded half a mile distant. At the old Assembly Rooms, a billiard table was washed away and, curious to relate, was found three or four days later washed ashore at Cuckmere".

A letter, now with Seaford Museum, from Mr Hermann Ebbinghaus to a relative, describes the day: "People were fain to save their lives and its force was so as to smash everything to little pieces. I was in my house. I groped my way through the water and was very near to being knocked down a trap in the cellar. The water came up to my chin."

The tidal inflow affected towns and villages all the way along the coast. "The chief consolation", wrote the *Hastings and St Leonard's Chronicle* "is that no loss of life has arisen. The damage is to property only, though there can be no assuming what permanent dangers to health may arise from the intense excitement, nor of the after-effects of damp in the hundreds of inundated houses which the forenoon of Sunday witnessed".

In Seaford, Hastings and other East Sussex coastal resorts it was a gale "unequalled within the memory of man or within received tradition". Intense rain fell for eight hours and this was accompanied by thunder and lightning. Hastings registered more than an inch which was greatly in excess of discharge by the ordinary outlets. The Priory stream was the first to overflow and great swirling torrents surged through the town, flooding basements and damaging stock with a mixture of water, clay and sediment. From the railway, looking up the valley, there was one vast lake of water a good six feet deep.

The foul weather became fouler as a south-west gale blew in. The moon was full and the tide became increasingly higher. By Sunday morning, the fourth day of the storm, mountainous waves "such as are never seen off the Hastings shore poured over the parade walls in a continuous raging torrent". Townsfolk had done what they could to barricade their homes but it was futile. "It was", said one inhabitant "like trying to keep the sea back with a broom".

The water gushed through George Street, West Street, Pelham Street and around the Albert Memorial Tower. It surrounded the Queen's Hotel and ran down Meadow Road, Middle Street and Station Road. The policeman on duty near York Hotel was waist deep in water and still it was rising. He refused to leave his post. The inhabitants were paralysed with fear. They looked at the raging seas and the heavy clouds beyond and waited anxiously for the midnight tide. Everywhere people were drenched to their skins but all Sunday afternoon they continued barricading and securing with one eye fixed on the heaving seas. In the evening the winds changed. The moon still shone brightly but the seas lulled.

Hastings had suffered a great public disaster. "It is sickening to enter house after house", said the *Chronicle*, "and see such heartbreaking scenes, especially those inhabited by the poorer people whose life, at the best, is a struggle with poverty. Everything is damaged beyond the hope of future utility. Mr Moon, baker and grocer, had the shop door burst open by the sea. Mr Saunders's stock of wines and spirits was battered into fragments. In the eastward part of the town not one house escaped. We are confident it is not an exaggeration to say that 256 dwellings is the lowest computation which can be made of those who have suffered".

A famous Moxon painting of the great storm of 1875 that caused the people of Seaford to run for their lives when the sea forced its way into the town centre. In the foreground is a damaged bathing machine and, in the distance, Seaford Head. Twenty five years earlier, in 1850, a large part of the Head was blown up, in the hope that fallen rocks would form a groyne to prevent shingle being carried out of the bay. Too much explosive was used and the mass of small pieces of chalk that came down did nothing to alleviate the situation.

CRASHING SPIRE

21st February, 1861: The tower and spire of Chichester Cathedral, already structurally unsound, collapsed in a violent storm. Massive timbers had been shoring up the building while repair work continued, when a workman saw a huge stone falling. Ninety minutes after the labourers had been evacuated, about 6,000 tons of masonry fell straight into the Cathedral. No-one was injured.

SUNDAY DINNERS

1st September, 1883: The entire South of England was badly hit by the tail end of a hurricane from the West Indies. Small craft were wrecked all along the coast, bathing machines overturned and many houses flooded. In some areas, people who had taken their Sunday dinners to be cooked at the bake house had to collect them by boat. The storm swept on into Kent.

The great Victorian blizzard

18th January, 1881

MOONLIGHT skating sessions on the thick ice at Angmering and other frozen lakes of Sussex became a favourite nocturnal activity in the bitterly cold days of early January, 1881. The nights were starry, still and quite magical but on the 17th came a gale so severe, that the snow which accompanied it was blown through every conceivable crack in windows, doors and roofs.

People awakened by the shrieking wind found that tiny ice crystals had been blasted through hair-line crevices and snow lay deep inside their homes. The *West Sussex Gazette* wrote: "What made matters worse was the wind - not the kind we are accustomed to - but cold, icy blasts, as if fresh from the Siberian deserts. It swooped down on one, laden with snowflakes, danced about one, so to speak, blowing in one's face whichever way one turned".

All communication between Brighton and Arundel was severed and the community of Burpham was isolated along with many other Sussex villages. Supplies had to be brought on the River Arun; the mail service ground to a halt and trains became snowbound. One lady travelling from Brighton on the 7 a.m. did not arrive in Arundel until 9.30 am the following day. Another passenger was on the train for 30 hours before he arrived in London. In Horsham, a special meeting of the Winter Fund and Relief Committee was held.

The snow-storm also severely disrupted the skating season. During the previous cold days thousands had gathered at Warnham Mill Pond, near Horsham and large parties patronised the splendid New England Pond in Cuckfield Park. On Sunday 16th January, hundreds visited the Decoy at Angmering where "the ice was in capital condition and they indulged to their hearts' content; the expanse of ice being large enough to permit the most free indulgences possible in the sport anywhere, perhaps, in this part of the country".

On the Sunday night, "the cold was stronger still". The *West Sussex Gazette* claimed: "The air was still clear, the night bright with the moonlight and there being more than 20 degrees of frost. In the night of Monday, however, a change came o'er the spirit of our dream. The wind, during the hours of darkness, simply howled and was accompanied by a heavy fall of snow".

In Brighton, nearly all the shops were shut. In Crawley, the snow drifted to the first floor windows. In Lewes, a gang of men attempted to extricate the train from London. In Chichester, postmen presented "a woebegone appearance, being encrusted with snow and icicles." In Portfield and Wickham, a hearse carrying a coffin was snowed in and had to be lifted over the wall to the city cemetery.

There were efforts, of course, to clear the snow but this was as "fruitless as Dame Partington when she tried to dry up the Atlantic with her mop".

'Huge rocks in a bloodstained sea'

16th January, 1884

ON the morning of the 27th August, 1883 in the narrow Sunda Straits between Java and Sumatra, a stupendous detonation occurred on the tiny uninhabited island of Krakatoa. This cataclysmic eruption had a force 26 times as powerful as the energy exerted from the greatest hydrogen bomb so far detonated and flung ash a quarter of a million feet into the upper atmosphere. The explosion awoke people from their slumbers more than 2,000 miles away

The ash was swept several times round the earth by high level winds and resulted in some of the most spectacular sunsets ever seen. From his Crowborough Observatory, Mr Leeson Prince wrote of the memorable evening of the 16th January, 1884. "On the morning of that day a dense fog rested on Crowborough Hill but shortly before noon the fog sank somewhat from its summit, the observatory alone being above it.

"Just upon sunset the usual violet tint became visible near the sun and a pinkish haze above, which extended nearly to the zenith - a sure commencement of a brilliant display. Upon the horizon and for about three degrees above it the sky soon assumed a decidedly green colour which very shortly changed to a brilliant scarlet band which extended from SE to WNW points on the horizon.

"The upper surface of the fog was heaped up into irregular and undulating masses and by degrees became lit up with a beautiful pink colour and had the appearance of huge rocks arising from a bloodstained sea. The scene was magnificent."

Eastgate Square, Chichester in January, 1881.

Shoreham in the snow of 1881. The buildings on the right today house the Marlipins Museum. The origin of this unusual name remains a mystery. The museum building was occupied by W.A.Gates, builder and undertaker in 1881.

Hastings beach on a fine summer's day before the turn of the century. The "Albertine", seen here drawn up on the beach, was for many years famous for its pleasure trips. In the background, opposite Carlisle Parade and Robertson Terrace are the bathing machines.

The Kursaal in Bexhill was always most popular on a fine day. A cycle boulevard was opened here in 1896 and the first motor races in England were held here in 1902.

Golden weather for a golden day. The ladies of Lewes, protected from the hot sun by parasols, and their straw-hatted menfolk flocked to the town centre on 21st June, 1887 to celebrate the 50th anniversary of the reign of Queen Victoria. The weather also smiled and the Sussex Express wrote: "The month of June (1887) will be remembered for its brilliancy, genial warmth and great drought".

Nightmare in the snow

9th - 13th March, 1891

JUST weeks after the tenth anniversary of the 1881 blizzard, Sussex endured another of Mother Nature's momentous snow-storms which caused deaths on sea and land, as well as widespread disruption to everyday life.

The blizzard began during the morning of Monday 9th March, 1891. By the evening, snow was laying thickly and theatregoers in Brighton, as they left a production of *The World,* found their carriages at the doors "white with driven snow".

At Hastings, three fishermen lost their lives in the heaving seas. Henry Brasier and Charles Phillips were thrown from the wreck of the *Henrietta* after it smashed into a groyne two miles east of Bexhill. George Phillips was the sole survivor. Almost insensible from cold, he staggered ashore and told how they had been tossed into the sea when the sails were blown away. In another incident, Harry Adams, a 20-year-old fisherman was drowned off the Lifeboat House at Hastings.

Many ships lit red flares as they approached the shore but in this blinding snow-storm the lights were blurred and their positions could not be pinpointed. A fishing boat, the *Welcome Home* got into difficulties near Beachy Head. The crew scrambled off the vessel at 11.30 p.m. and walked all night in the gale. They arrived at Newhaven suffering from exposure.

At Seaford the crew of a beached fishing craft climbed the cliffs and wandered about all night. Seaford was severed from the outside world by the snow but the fishermen eventually found the town

and enjoyed a hearty breakfast. They learned that the body of the chief boatman had been discovered on the beach. West of Littlehampton, a fishing vessel, the *James and John* was beached and totally wrecked. A schooner, *The Scout* arrived at Newhaven after being in collison with a ship. Her sails had been torn away in the gale.

On land, an elderly shepherd died from the cold at Bramber Farm, North Mundham and an elderly broom-maker from Maresfield was found dead in the snow at Nutley. Between Piddinghoe and Lewes a mailcoach driver, John Luck was "rendered almost insensible by the cold wind". His horse went on its way without the control of the driver and was stopped at the Anchor Inn at Ringmer.

The Hassocks cart left Lewes at the same time but got only as far as Courthouse. The Uckfield cart didn't even set off and the one from Seaford reached Spring Farm on the Tuesday only to find snow over the tops of hedges - a story repeated all over Sussex. At Eastbourne the mailcoach driver reached Willingdon by taking his horse over ploughed fields. He went on towards Horsham but became embedded in snow and had to be dug out. Two mailcoaches on the London-Brighton service were trapped at Staplefield, neither driver knowing they were only half a mile apart. The snow was up to the bellies of the horses and they had to be dug out.

The depression which brought this spectacular storm eventually moved away north-eastwards along the English Channel and warmer, westerly winds brought a thaw.

Ha'penny dinners for the hungry

Winter of 1895

THE winter of 1895 was notable for a penetrating frost which made an appearance in early January and returned with a vengeance later in the month and through most of February. It was also the month when Britain's lowest-ever temperature was recorded: -17 F (-27.2C) at Braemar. This was to be equalled in January, 1982.

The intense cold caused some bizarre incidents. Firemen's hoses and buckets froze solid at a fire on Worthing seafront, the curtain at the Lyric Theatre came down during a show when the hydraulic machinery froze, a fancy dress carnival was held on

the ice at Hassocks and a cricket match was staged at Ferring before the beleaguered football season had time to recover from the attacks by the weather.

Poor people suffered considerably. A fund to provide free breakfasts was set up in Worthing and the town arranged ha'penny dinners for the unemployed and hungry. Conditions for skating were "splendid" all over Sussex. In Petworth Park the ice was six to eight inches thick and on Warnham Lake, hundreds of Horshamites "availed themselves of the moonlit evenings to skate on the patches which had been swept of snow".

This photograph is almost certainly the Brighton to London parcel mailcoach stuck fast in a raging blizzard at Staplefield, near Cuckfield on Tuesday 10th March, 1891. On the previous night both the "down" coach from London and the "up" coach from Brighton were hampered by some of the most appalling conditions ever known in Sussex. One driver trudged through the snow to reach The Jolly Tanners while the other led his horses through the snow-storm to The Red Lion at Handcross.

The West Pier at Brighton was also badly damaged in the 1896 storm.

Chain Pier is washed away

4th December, 1896

THE old Suspension Chain Pier at Brighton, which had been opened in such great style in 1823, was totally destroyed in a furious storm which hit the Sussex coast during the night of 4th December, 1896. The West Pier at Brighton was also badly damaged, along with Volk's electric railway and many buildings. The passing of the Pier was fully reported in the *Brighton Gazette* on the day after the storm.

"In the height of the gale which raged last night the Chain Pier was completely washed away, except a few timbers of the first pile from the shore. A heavy sea was running all day and as the tide rose in the evening the waves dashed with great fury against the already injured structure. At ten to eleven, a few minutes before the tide reached its highest, the famous landmark broke up with a series of reports which sounded, in the fury of the wind and the waves, not much louder than pistol shots.

"The chains snapped asunder and sank and in a few minutes nothing remained but the previously mentioned group of piles and two small pavilions which marked the entrance. To the east of the Pier, Volk's Railway was further carried away together with whole stretches of the roadway, several feet in depth. The scene is a remarkable one, as desolate as anything could be imagined. The news spread rapidly through the town and many people turned out to verify the report themselves. Though the night was as black as threatening clouds could make it, the foam of the sea showing against the few piles left, served to make it only too clear that the Pier really had gone."

October gales of that year had caused considerable damage to the Chain Pier and the newspaper explained how the head was as much as six feet out of the perpendicular. The corporation had invited tenders for its purchase and removal but it was "little anticipated that a south east gale would so quickly and so effectively lay the historic structure level with the sands."

On the Saturday, the day after the storm, there was a great crowd of sightseers and on the Sunday it reached quite phenomenal proportions. Although the Pier's foundations remained visible at low tide until 1949, there is now no sign of it although the two small kiosks were saved and later placed near the Palace Pier.

The Chain Pier - just a few timbers remained on the first pile from the shore.

The great spring drought

17th March - 15th May, 1893

A SUSSEX drought almost without parallel began in March, continued into April and ended 60 days later, on 15th May, with a few drops of rain. In parts of London there was no rain for 73 days . In meteorological history it is known as the "famous spring drought of 1893".

During March, Eastbourne experienced a daily average of seven hours of sunshine and much early sea bathing was enjoyed. April produced a magnificent Easter Bank Holiday. Thousands flocked to Brighton and on the West Pier alone 24,000 people poured past the turnstiles in just two days.

In the countryside, the banks and woods were swarming with wild flowers. The rhododendrons showed rich masses of colour and the clear call of the cuckoo was heard early in April. However, as the sun continued to shine relentlessly, vegetation became exhausted and tinder dry. Huge fires broke out. South of Tunbridge Wells about a mile of undergrowth was destroyed in the Broadwater Forest near Rusthall. For the crowds viewing from elevated positions in the Spa town, it provided a spectacular sight.

In early May the scarcity of primroses prevented their traditional use for Brighton's dome decorations. The Hurstpierpoint Root Show was abandoned. Roads were thick with dust and there was a plague of wasps. On 15th May it rained and a story is told of one Sussex man saying to another: "For goodness sake, sir, let's get indoors so it can fall on the ground". It ended 60 days of absolute drought recorded from Lewes to Haywards Heath.

At Eastbourne only 1.8 inches (30mm) of rain fell between 28th February and 3rd July of this incredible year. Throughout the county, wells ran dry and many people were in great distress. In Crowborough, the two public springs maintained an ancient reputation for being inexhaustible, to the delight of the inhabitants.

In the latter half of July a number of showers helped Sussex to slake its great thirst.

Hailstones were the size of golf balls

30th May, 1897

HAILSTONES the size of golf balls fell at Seaford and Selmeston on 30th May, 1897 during a storm which was tracked by the well-known Sussex meteorologist, Mr C. Leeson Prince from his observatory high up on Crowborough Hill. He wrote: "This was one of the most memorable thunderstorms within living memory. Although it occurred at a distance of nearly 20 miles from this house its elevated position enabled me to watch its progress for a considerable time.

"Soon after three o'clock, very heavy electric clouds appeared over the South Downs near Newhaven and for some time remained almost stationary. Soon after six o'clock a line of Nimbus cloud, two or three miles in length, of a whitish appearance exhibited a well-defined edge on its northern side and any further advance of the storm in our direction was checked. After passing over Seaford and Selmeston it rapidly increased its pace and finally disappeared to the east.

"Over Selmeston, accompanied by a furious wind it struck the vicarage with great force and hailstones dashed through no less than 25 panes of glass".

These hailstones are not the famous "golf ball variety" which fell at Seaford and Selmeston. This particular plateful are among those which bombarded Ticehurst and Wadhurst 11 years later on 4th June, 1908.

CHAPTER THREE

The Edwardian Years

The Edwardian years were dominated, weatherwise, by the remarkable months between January, 1908 and March, 1909. In January, freezing rain brought down telephone wires in East Sussex. In April, a snowstorm caused great disasters at sea. In June, hailstones the size of pigeon's eggs fell near Wadhurst. In December, it snowed again and by March, 1909, the people of Sussex really felt under the weather.

29th July, 1901: A deluge at Wadhurst, Ticehurst and Cousley Wood gave as much as 3.25 inches of rain in less than an hour.

14th May, 1902: A sharp frost destroyed much fruit at Lewes. In June at Pyecombe, clouds of hot steam poured out of the ground for several minutes on the south slopes of Wolstonbury Hill. It was not continuous but small children danced in the warmth.

22nd February, 1903: At Crowborough the rain was of a remarkable colour and consistency, being thick and of a dirty reddish colour. It was a wet year in West Sussex and at Midhurst just over 51 inches (1303 mm) of rain fell.

January 14th, 1904: A violent squall blew down a stack of chimneys at the Princes Hotel, Hove, smashing the roof and badly injuring a lady in one of the bedrooms. Overall it was a good year for farmers and at Ticehurst, the hay crop was wonderful.

31st October, 1905: Great waves lashed into fury by a high wind broke onto the Worthing foreshore. The local newspaper reported that "a good many persons foolishly attempted to pass along Beach Parade when the waves were breaking over. The majority found themselves helplessly shut in between the sea and the stone wall at the mercy of the waves, to the amusement of the crowd at Splash Point.

September, 1906: Most of Sussex enjoyed a record September heatwave early in the month. Even at Crowborough, nearly 800 feet above sea level, the temperature reached 90.9 F (32.7C). On Christmas night heavy snow fell reaching a depth of five to six inches. February, 1907 also had snow.

September, 1907: An observer at Heathfield wrote of this month: "In the first few days one almost lost heart fighting the weeds but thanks to the finest September ever remembered they were conquered. There were no gales, no floods and no worries, except for squirrels and mice".

Snowbound Rye in January, 1908.

The booty on the beaches

1st March, 1901

WHEN the Worthing lifeboat, the *Henry Harris*, went out into the jaws of a south-west gale to the aid of a large steamer in distress, it took more than two and a half hours to reach the vessel which was two miles out to sea. The crew found just a wreck with only the bow and masts clear of the water. They could read the name, *The Indiana* of Hull but there was no sign of life.

Meanwhile there was frantic activity on the beach. Tens of thousands of oranges and lemons were drifting ashore. The beach was crowded. Townspeople of all ages were scrambling for free fruit, some with baskets and some with horse-drawn trolleys. As the beach was cleared people began to rush into the breakers and fights broke out over the spoils.

The lifeboat returned under sail at 10 am, two hours after the first beachcomber had discovered the booty. They had no news of the lost crew of *The Indiana*. Everyone thought there had been a dreadful tragedy, especially when the ship's log book was washed ashore. The ship, carrying 2,225 tons and 227 feet long had left Swansea for Venice on 18th December, 1900. Captain Fred Kershaw and his crew had made many ports of call.

The full story unfolded in the afternoon when it transpired that *The Indiana*, in thick fog had run amidships into an oil steamer, *The City of Washington*. The crew, however, were rescued and taken to Newhaven. Meanwhile, with the abandoned ship breaking up, the exotic cargo was being washed ashore all down the coast. There were oranges and lemons in Seaford and Newhaven, a barrel of wine in Brighton and a broad yellow band of lemons at Shoreham.

A violent thunderstorm which hit the Uckfield area on 17th August, 1905 caused considerable damage to property. The photograph shows Ingle Cottage, Uckfield after a "fireball" had engulfed the entire length of the roof.

The River Adur, which neatly divides the villages of Bramber and Upper Beeding, frequently flooded and a popular event was the almost annual "tub race" from one village to the other. It is a tradition which continues today - on the river, rather than the road! The photograph was taken on 2nd February, 1904 during an exceptional flood.

1st November, 1905 and the people of Hastings could hardly believe their eyes. There on the promenade is an enormous crater, more than nine feet deep and full of sea water. It had been caused by the kind of gale that Hastings residents became accustomed to, only on this occasion the promenade had been battered and bruised by some of the biggest waves ever seen. More rough seas were to follow but on the 29th December the weather did an about-turn and the air pressure reached a remarkable 30.96 inches (1048 millibars).

Boom years for Camber Sands

THE picture of the Edwardian lady tentatively testing the temperature of the water at Camber Sands accompanied a story in an old book of Rye about the balmy year of 1906 in which the mercury, on September lst, rose to 96F (35.5C), then a record for that month. August, too, was hot and sunny with just the occasional isolated thunderstorm.

The *Sussex Express* in its issue of 11th August, 1906 reported: "The number of visitors to Rye on Saturday and Monday must have constituted a record holiday crowd for the old town. On Monday especially, the number of visitors was abnormally large, and the majority betook themselves to the quietude of Camber Sands where, it is stated, there had never been such a crowd before. The Tram Company carried upwards of 2,000 passengers to this delightful spot".

That does not include those who walked, cycled or drove, either by horse and carriage or the automobile. These were boom years for the Sussex coastal resorts. The holiday trade was the county's most flourishing and highly developed industry and every town from Rye to Selsey competed for a share in the "sunshine market". Local businessmen and outside investors had already built their piers and promenades but hotels and theatres, letting houses and landladies, were cropping up everywhere.

For the day trippers and the longer stayers August was always the most popular month, due to school holidays and to the additional day off - Bank Holiday Monday which had been introduced in 1871. 1906 was an exceptional year but the Bank Holiday weather in Sussex in 1908 was destined to be the sunniest on record.

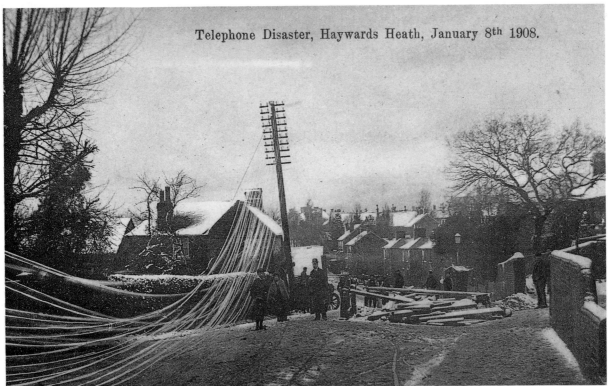

Telephone Disaster, Haywards Heath, January 8th 1908.

Residents of "The Heath" as Haywards Heath was affectionately known could hardly believe their eyes. More than one and a half miles of telephone wires between the town and Wivelsfield were spectacularly draped across the main road, and many buildings badly damaged.

The culprit was a strong blizzard accompanied by violent winds and then freezing rain on 8th January, 1908, which held fast to everything it touched. The weight of the snow and ice was too much for the telephone wires. Encouraged by the wind, they sagged and sagged and eventually crashed to the ground. This caused some havoc to the communications between London and Brighton and telephone calls took three hours to get through.

In 1908 Haywards Heath was, according to Hillaire Belloc, "a town of the London sort". It originally grew up around a lonely railway station to serve Cuckfield in 1841.

*Telephone communication was rather wayward in Haywards Heath on 8th January, 1908.
Little wonder with poles at this angle in Church Road.*

LAUNCH OF THE HASTINGS LIFEBOAT. APRIL 25. 1908.
NO. 5. SNOWING HEAVILY. 6.40 P.M. PHOTO BY JUDGES'

The gallant crew of the Charles Arkcoll sets off into the teeth of a raging blizzard on 25th April, 1908.

Tragedy in an April blizzard

25th April, 1908

SIX days before May in 1908, winter returned to Sussex with a vengeance. A snowstorm, which would have been notable in any January, blew up on 25th April with "extreme severity". At Brighton, the white mantle which buried spring flowers, was five inches deep and in Hampshire drifts reached a depth of six feet.

The days leading up to the weekend of 25th - 26th April were unseasonably cold. Saturday, the 25th, began with sunshine and showers but it was in the late afternoon that a blinding snowstorm blew with "terrific force" for two hours. The wind was so strong that a barrow loaded with furniture toppled over in Pelham Road, Seaford and the annual fair at Crowborough, with its coconut shies, swing boats and other traditional fairground attractions, was forced to close.

No-one in Tunbridge Wells could remember such a sight in April. The historic Calverley Road open market, with its vegetables, fish and other stalls bore the full force of the blizzard and vendors had almost to guess at what articles they sold from the curiously-shaped coverings of wind-driven snow.

At sea, the picture was grim. Vessels ran into great trouble and a terrible disaster occurred near Portsmouth. Unable to see through a blizzard, a cruiser, *The Gladiator* collided with an American liner, causing the deaths of 34 people who perished in the cold water. At the same time at St. Leonard's, thousands gathered in driving sleet to watch the Hastings lifeboat, *Charles Arkcoll* go to the aid of a London barge in distress. The lifeboat was launched as the blizzard raged and both boats were blown at great speed by the westerly gale. The barge had snapped a cable but *Charles Arkcoll* caught up with her and accompanied her to Dungeness, where the crew spent a sleepless night.

In meteorological terms, the snow occurred when a low pressure area became embedded in a cold northerly airstream over Sussex.

A rare witchery of beauty

28th December, 1908

"THOSE who have been hungering for an old-fashioned Christmastide found their wishes gratified this morning, snow falling so heavily throughout Sussex that probably by the end of the day everyone will have had more than enough to satisfy their longing for real winter weather".

So said the *Brighton Evening Argus* on Tuesday 29th December, 1908 after a snowfall which was reminiscent of 1881. Great flakes fell on an absolutely dry ground and a strong wind blew with considerable force. In the case of the 1881 blizzard the snow fell at night but as this late December progressed it looked as if the quantity would equal the memorable experience of nearly 28 years ago. By five o'clock there was a depth of one foot of snow in thoroughfares where it lay undisturbed by traffic.

There was a remarkable sight at the Olympic Skating Rink at Brighton where snow was percolating through the roof and covering the floor. The rink was closed for the first time in many years. In Eastbourne the Corporation buses were taken off the road after one had difficulty on Meads Hill. Many buses had to be towed into the depot. Goods, however, were delivered as quickly as possible by men and boys but even small hand carts required two persons to push them through the snow. Terminus Road was deserted. So fierce was the blizzard on the sea front that the snow and mist rendered the sea invisible.

Passengers on the 11.40 am from Victoria had an uncomfortable journey when the train came to a standstill in the middle of the Clayton Tunnel. Fog signals had to be placed on the line as a warning to an oncoming train and the driver ran into Brighton with information of the mishap.

The vigorous task of clearing the streets of East Sussex fell under the direction of the various corporation surveyors. In Brighton more than 1,000 men were at work the following day shovelling, sweeping, loading, carting and dumping. Around 500 of these were the unemployed, who faced up to their formidable task throughout a day in which the sun shone brilliantly.

At Hastings, where the tramway service was suspended, there was great excitement over the prospect of the skating season starting early as the temperature plunged to 23.6F (-4.5C) but Alexandra Park was still marked with danger signs. At Haywards Heath, Horsham, Lewes and Uckfield there were strong drifts and "all horses had to be walked." At Hove, 290 extra men and 85 horses were employed.

The snow was carted away and thrown onto the beach.

The Brighton Herald in reporting that 224,000 tons of snow had been cleared wrote: "There is nothing that so utterly transforms a town as such a fall of snow as that of this week. It brings with it a rare witchery of beauty, yet a rare sense of desolation. The beauty is in the encrusting of the trees, the silvering of the bushes and the mantling of lawns of purest white. The effect of desolation was heightened by the profound hush. Indeed the strange effect of deep snow to the townsman is the silence that it brings".

In all East Sussex coastal towns, business was at a standstill. In the great drapery establishments the assistants grouped themselves around the stove and gazed out at the strange aspect of the outer world. *The Herald* said: "In Islington Road a man made a couch in the snow. Here he was found insensible, though not from the cold. He was removed to the cells and had to answer next morning to the Magistrates. He was lucky for he would have slept the sleep of death."

By the middle of January there was a great change in the climate, a thaw set in and the snow began to fall off the roofs in avalanche fashion with heavy rain washing it away. As the ice on the lakes thinned there was a tragedy at Eridge where two men from Frant were drowned. By the time their funeral service was held, it was again snowing heavily.

By March, Sussex was suffering again from blinding snowfalls, accompanied by frequent north-easterly gales, which were sufficiently bad on the third for the King to postpone his journey to Biarritz.

Eastbourne Promenade in December, 1908.

The sea front at Eastbourne during the blizzard of 28th-29th December, 1908 when the snow and mist combined to render the sea invisible.

The clearing up begins in Eastbourne.

The tramway service in Brighton was suspended during the blizzard of December, 1908 but, thanks to the sterling efforts of the Corporation snow-clearers, they were soon running again.

Postmen had great difficulty in December, 1908 delivering the mail, especially in rural areas, but they always turned up for duty...and for the photographer !

The snow brought a rare witchery of beauty, said the local newspaper. Certainly Arundel Castle looked magnificent with its snow-covered battlements in December, 1908.

The Eastbourne Road at Cross In Hand, early in January, 1909. The old school house is seen on the right.

Snow that glittered like diamonds

March, 1909

HAVING survived the rigours of January and February, the beleaguered people of Sussex were looking forward to spring as March, 1909 arrived. Despite their hopes it began with severe frosts and heavy snowfalls. Football matches were cancelled, trade in town centres badly affected and bird life was threatened. There were scenes of great beauty, too.

Thick, feathery flakes floated down in calm conditions on 2nd March and at East Grinstead "there was scarely a puff of wind to disturb anything.....snow hung to the branches of skeleton trees as though white piping had been used to give their figures a more prominent display".

An observer of the moonlit Sussex countryside wrote on 4th March: "The white expanse glitters with a million diamonds, and tree and bush stand out like a clear etching against the white background. The silence is absolute, so that the crisp crunch of the frozen snow beneath the feet seems an intrusion".

At Pevensey Marshes, a handful of oats scattered on the ground brought down clouds of famished birds "so tame you could catch them in your hands".

There was also tragedy. A boy of eight fell on the ice in Elm Road, Portslade, hit his head and died.

Eastbourne at night - "the tree stands out like a clear etching. The silence is absolute."

CHAPTER FOUR

Unrest on the weather front

Thunder, lightning, deluges, storms and floods. In the years between 1910 and 1920 the elements combined their considerable forces to change the face of the landscape. Pagham's great harbour was reclaimed by the sea, and much of Selsey was washed away. Worthing pier was dismantled by the wind and Bungalow Town received a drubbing. The most extraordinary year was 1911 when Sussex was hit by every type of weather variation possible, including a heatwave. The temperature rose to the nineties and, at Hayward's Heath, 90F was exceeded on 10 days in the summer.

1912: A severe gale on 4th-5th March damaged the colonnade deck at Bexhill-on-Sea. December was extremely mild and 40 bunches of primroses were gathered around Warbleton Church for use as Christmas decorations.

1913: A stormy sea swept away Worthing Pier shortly before midnight on 22nd March. After a wet October, further torrential rain flooded many roads in the Littlehampton and Arundel districts on 12th November. The rain was so heavy, visibility was reduced to just a few yards.

1914: An autumn drought of 25 days from 17th September to 12th October caused a dearth of many winter vegetables at Mayfield. In December there was a deluge. Nearly 10 inches (250mm) of rain fell at Balcombe with 11.54 inches (294mm) at Linchmere.

1914-1915: During the winter, rain fell on three days out of every four at Brighton.

1916: The second half of February through March was very wintry. There were 11 separate visitations of snow in the Brighton district. A fall of four inches was recorded on 26th February. In north-west Sussex, the rivers were swollen on 28th March by heavy rain, and mud-coloured torrents swept down from the hills. Pulborough became a vast lake.

1917: Continuously cold from January to April. Not within living memory had vegetation growth been so belated, with a chill wind blowing through the leafless boughs of April, and snow falling on seven days.

1918: January lit up the South Coast with 81 hours of sunshine, outstanding for mid-winter. A cold spell brought a carpet of snow and temperatures below freezing, even by day, around 8th January.

1919: A chilly year, especially in the autumn, but the saying - "if there's ice in November that will bear a duck, there'll be nothing after but sludge and muck", came true. December was mild and wet.

Shingle beach in town. The aftermath of the March, 1913 storm in Hastings.

This dramatic picture was taken at Hastings on 2nd August, 1906. The storm moved north over Sussex and when it hit Guildford extensive damage was caused. It was accompanied by a tornado. Trees were torn up and people killed.

Fiery serpent in the sky

IN a series of violent thunderstorms which struck East Sussex during the summer of 1909, a man was killed on the downs, the driver of a milk cart was knocked from his seat, the walls of a bedroom at Portslade were split from top to bottom, a chimney stack was sent dramatically crashing through the roof of a house in Brighton and lightning traversed tramway lines like a blue flame.

The *Brighton Herald* noticed a "curious parallel" between the storms which broke overhead with startling suddenness. The most severe was the one which caused so much damage to 2, Ventnor Villas when lightning struck the chimney which toppled sending masses of masonry onto the street. Two servants in the house escaped serious injury but were extremely frightened.

Less than a year later, on 5th June, 1910 came a storm that was "remarkable for its duration and for the overwhelming effects of the thunder, which set basements rattling and floors trembling under the fury of its cannonading". The *Brighton Herald* likened it to a fiery serpent which shot across the sky at terrific pace, its long tail stretched across the luminous canopy. "It was majestically grand, but nature was in one of her angriest moods and when the prodigious forces run riot, as they did on Sunday night, the might and majesty of the demonstration carries a certain sense of awe".

The storm destroyed the picuresque villa to the north of Withdean. The Priory was struck by lightning and the ensuing fire consumed the building. Every flash of lightning set the alarm bells ringing in Brighton and the firemen had to attend them all, lest a real call should come. One did. A man galloped in on horseback with news of a fire at Bevendean. It was outside the Borough boundary

The Priory at Withdean was struck by lightning on 5th June, 1910 and the ensuing fire "consumed the building."

but the gallant Volunteer Section from Duke Street promptly went to the scene.

The crew of a mackerel boat had a sensational experience during the height of the storm when, surrounded by great blue flames, they lost consciousness. When they recovered they found the mast was split, bolts were forced out of their sockets and an iron hatch was riddled with holes. There were many casualties in this storm but only one fatality when an elderly woman died of fright. In many households the children were so terrified that they could not be pacified and next morning numbers were kept away from school.

The *Herald* described one hardy person who watched the storm from one end of the promenade. "Here, indeed, was a modern Ajax."

BOUR RECLAIMED BY THE SEA   DECR 1910
SIDLESHAM

The sea breached the shingle banks at Pagham and five square miles were submerged in less than an hour.

Pagham Harbour reclaimed

16th December, 1910

CHRISTMAS, 1910 was a forbidding one for the people of Selsey. Torrential rain, a week earlier, had flooded the gasworks so there were no lights and those without candles spent the Yuletide in darkness. The entire south coast was ravaged by gale-force winds and floods and at Selsey more than two inches (50 mm) of rain lashed the area, swamping 5,000 acres of pastureland. The main road from Chichester was flooded, as was the railway line and the tramline south of Sidlesham. Livestock had to be rescued by men in boats.

At Pagham, a sand and shingle bank known as the "Narrows" gave way not far from the old entrance to the harbour. The sea poured in and, in less than an hour, four to five thousands acres of land were flooded. From the west the sea also breached the shingle banks at Medmerry and Ham, submerging altogether five square miles.

Pagham Harbour had been reclaimed in 1876 but, in just a few hours, the storm of 1910 undid all the work, returning the area to its former state. It was only the narrow bank at the old ferry of Selsey which prevented a complete union of floodwater. The light railway was destroyed, two miles of its track being washed away. It was not reinstated until June, 1911.

The *Daily News* on 19th December reported that "Selsey has been an island in the English Channel", and an old fisherman, talking about the worst floods he had ever seen, commented: "Men drove the fish away from Sidlesham and, you see, God has brought them back".

December, 1910. Children play in the flood water near Sidlesham Mill. This tidal mill was pulled down in 1913, having become redundant when the harbour was closed. The foundations can be seen today just west of the public house, The Crab and Lobster.

The light railway from Chichester to Selsey was completed on 2nd September, 1897 for
£12,000. On 16th December, 1910 the sea broke through the bank on the eastern side of the
peninsular and covered two miles of track between Chalder and Ferry with water 12 feet deep
in places. Sidlesham station was flooded at high tide.

Coast erosion at Bexhill-on-Sea in January, 1910. The inscription on the back of this postcard
reads: "My dear friends, I thought you would like a card of our damaged seafront. We have not
got much and what we have is nearly all washed away. It has been something dreadful lately.
I will send you a local paper so that you will be able to read about it." Dated 30th January.

Bramber in 1911 when the River Adur once again burst its banks.

Winds, snow, drought, floods

Four seasons of 1911

LIKE an apple tree in a prolific season, there are some years which become overloaded with weather events. Such a year was 1911.

On 22nd March the mercury soared to 62F (17C) at Brighton and the strong rays of the sun caused a massive shoal of fish to swim near the surface on which flocks of gulls gratefully foraged. Within days there were strong winds and blizzards. A 28-foot high chimney crashed through the roof of a house in Old Town, Hastings, narrowly missing two people and two ships foundered in the Channel after colliding in heavy seas.

Before March was out, spring returned and the memory of the recent snow-storm was shaken off like a bad dream as people drove around in open carriages and motor cars. It did not last. By 5th April the vivid blue skies and dazzling sun alternated with blinding snow squalls in a bitter polar airstream. Snow lay nine inches deep in Battle and Seaford and four feet deep between Rotherfield and Mayfield. The Dyke Road to Patcham resembled a vast glacier. For the first time in the club's history a match was postponed at Brighton Football Club. Nine cargo steamers were storm bound off Brighton, unable to proceed. Many more sheltered in the lee of Beachy Head.

May brought the beginning of one of the most remarkable spells of weather ever experienced in

Sussex. There was sunshine, drought and heat well into September. In the Weald, huge fissures, caused by the contraction of clay in the baking sun, reached a depth of 14 feet. At Rudgwick, subsidence caused houses to sink. At Brighton, July brought an astonishing 380 hours of sunshine. Even on the dullest day there was five hours of sun.

In August the temperature rose to 98.6 F (37C) at Mayfield on the 9th. Ladies wore muslim and cotton frocks and men showed scant regard for conventional attire. Mineral water manufacturers were overwhelmed. The period between May and September yielded almost as much sun as the whole year of 1910. At Haywards Heath, a temperature of 90 F (32C) was maintained on 10 days.

As if to make up for the Mediterranean summer there followed a belt of low pressure systems, rain-laden and often windy. At Bepton, the summer had yielded just four inches (100mm) in rain while the last three months gave 23.65 inches. (591mm). Nothing normally disturbs the peace and quiet of Bramber in the winter, apart, that is, from the fear of flood. The heavy rains of November caused water to burst the banks of the Adur all down the valley from Ashurst, Partridge Green, Henfield, Steyning to Bramber. The inhabitants moved into upper rooms. Tradesmen delivered their wares in boats to customers leaning out of bedroom windows.

A large crowd watches the sea swirl around the memorial at Hastings .

Games with the waves

October, 1911

A HOLE 20 feet in diameter appeared in the promenade at Hastings during a gale which caused enormous damage to property in the centre of the town and, at its height, attracted a number of rather foolhardy spectators who played daring games with the waves.

The *Hastings and St. Leonard's Pictorial* said that a large crowd watched the waves roll in at a height rarely seen before in the Channel. "The wind which was blowing at hurricane force lashed them into boiling foam and the spectators found great amusement in approaching near to the railings on the sea front and then, as a wave broke over the parade, rushing helter skelter into back streets, jumping onto window sills, or clinging to lamp posts as the water swirled around them."

Caroline Parade had a tremendous buffeting.

"The waves literally shook the ground", said the newspaper "and it was not long after high tide that, with a crackling sound and a thud, the sea knocked a piece of coping onto the parade which had been extended at enormous expense and was only completed at the beginning of the year".

On this day in 1911 the sea was carried by the wind with a swishing noise into the town centre. The liveliest street scenes were around the Memorial. The clock tower was surrounded and the sea ran up Havelock Road and Wellington Place on one side and Middle Street and Station Road on the other. George Street looked like a river and the side roads a series of whirlpools. All the time shopkeepers stood helplessly behind their barricades as the water swirled in and out of doors and windows, tugging goods from shelves.

Worthing Pier laid to waste

22nd March, 1913

MANY great gales had hit the Sussex shores in the early years of the twentieth century and each in turn carried the almost predictable description of "the worst in living memory". The same graphic title was given to the Easter storm of 22nd March, 1913 but this wasn't journalistic licence. This time it was true.

The gale burst upon the Sussex coast on a Saturday night and wrecked Volk's Electric Railway at Brighton. It totally destroyed the Worthing Pier, swept away 15 homes at Bungalow Town and inflicted grievous damage on Lancing. All along the coast there was structural damage. Baulks of timber were floating in town centres, long sections of promenades were undermined and, at Brighton, the road from the Aquarium to the borough boundary was carpeted with hundreds of tons of shingle.

It was Worthing, not Brighton, which suffered most. At half past ten the pavilion on the pier was cleared of an audience who had watched the evening's entertainment. Soon after midnight a tremendous sea struck the pier and a huge derrick at the entrance was seen to sway. A moment later it fell with a crash. Loud reports were heard above the noise of the gale and three-quarters of the pier vanished into the brine. The whole town was plunged into darkness and at the electric light generating station the staff had to use candles.

The storm had developed with suddenness and violence. The sun had shone brightly on Saturday morning but at 4 o'clock there was a deluge of rain followed by a mighty gale which raged until 11 o'clock. It coincided with the highest tide of the year and, at midnight, the vernal equinox was reached. Then the wind changed direction to blow dead on to the shore.

At Bungalow Town, consisting mainly of railway carriage homes, 15 were removed by the sea and 15 more irretrievably damaged. No lives were lost but seven people were isolated in a "bungalow" where they had a terrifying experience until the receding tide permitted their release early on Sunday morning. The contour of the coast at Worthing was completely altered and only the main road which rested on a bed of clay stood between the sea and 500 acres of flooded land. The *Evening Argus* said that the community was smitten to its very foundation; dazed and crippled. "The little township reminded one somehow of a man who had suddenly become aged, toothless, crutched and tottering under a knockdown blow."

In the brilliant sunshine of Sunday afternoon and the warmer sun of Monday morning, the damage was a source of never-failing interest to the holiday crowds. It had been the most crowded Easter Brighton had ever known. Every hotel and boarding house was occupied and many, unable to get rooms, had gone back to London. Those who remained had plenty to see in Brighton...and then they went to Worthing. Cars, motorbikes and charabancs poured along the coast road only to find ,at Shoreham ,that it was impassable. So they took to the hills. A long, winding stream snaked its way through the little Saxon village of Sompting and villagers stared in amazement as this endless procession hurtled by, scattering the mud far and wide.

At Worthing they parked their vehicles and walked to Black Rock, a place of picturesque chaos where, according to the *Brighton Herald* "man and nature seem to be in eternal conflict to the detriment of both". Here they sat around as if at a theatre and gazed at the destruction before them. One man, with a business enterprise that seemed worthy of some reward, was selling postcards of the scene, but no-one wanted to buy. "What a life", he shouted. "Everybody asks me 'what is this and what is that' and I talk to them until I am dry as (a very hot place) and then they says 'thank you kindly' and goes away."

In the sunshine of this Monday morning the sea was as calm as a pond and the water was dotted with rowing boats. "It was hard to believe", reported *The Herald* "that this was the same sea that 30 hours before was battering Worthing to pieces." Away to the west, projected blackly against the glow of the sun, stood Worthing pierhead in "frowning isolation". A few feet of deck stretched landwards like a pointed finger. On the evening of Easter Monday animated pictures of the damage at Bungalow Town were being exhibited in London.

With the 1913 cricket season imminent, this was the county ground at Hastings.

Worthing Pier, before and after the great storm of 22nd-23rd March, 1913.

Soon after midnight on 22nd March, 1913, a tremendous sea struck the Pier and a huge derrick at the entrance was seen to sway. A moment later it fell with a crash and three quarters of the Pier vanished into the brine.

Bungalow Town, Worthing - a photograph taken on 23rd March, 1913.

Demise of Bungalow Town

22nd March, 1913

BUNGALOW Town was built on the south side of the mud flats bordering The Adur from railway carriages beyond restoration. They were sold to property speculators who had them towed by horses across the river. Sir Ralph Richardson (1902-1983) lived with his mother in two of these carriages when he was a boy, so it is possible that he had the terrifying experience of seeing 15 houses removed by the sea, and others irretrievably damaged in the famous Easter storm of 1913.

The term Bungalow Town was originally applied to all the shack and shanty buildings on the quieter coastal stretches. It was an aspect of unplanned growth from Camber to The Witterings before the 1914-18 war. Weekend residents erected any building which took their fancy - railway carriages, tramcars and more sophisticated structures with verandahs.

The inhabitants of the Bungalow Towns had not made any allowances for the fury of nature and they stood little chance in the face of a storm which was powerful enough to destroy an iron pier. The photographs of the wrecked bungalows at Shoreham and Lancing are ample evidence of the nightmare they must have suffered.

However, the carriages were still home, and every effort was made to restore them. Many were joined together by a tin roof and the space between them made a large room. In the 1930's, Bungalow Town at Shoreham supported a population as large as that of the old town itself. Most of the buildings were demolished at the beginning of the second world war when the beaches were protected against enemy invasion.

Wrecked bungalows on Lancing Beach after the storm of 22nd March, 1913.

Buckle Road, Seaford was badly flooded in the Easter storm of 1913.

Hailstones, the size and shape of tangerines, which fell on Tunbridge Wells and the area around the Kent and Sussex border on the afternoon of 25th May, 1922, smashed so many windows that suppliers ran out of replacement glass and hundreds of tons had to be ordered from London. This phenomenal storm came up the valley of the Weald, passed over the elevated ground at Southborough, drove into Tunbridge Wells, built up over the ridge of hills at Hawkenbury and vented its wrath on the border villages. The terrifying violence lasted just 15 minutes. The photograph above shows the hail piled high by the road at Southborough where shop assistants had to be carried to safety. Below, the boot of a car showing hailstone damage.

CHAPTER FIVE

The roaring twenties

Many spectacular weather events occurred in the twenties, including a horrific 15-minute hailstorm on the Sussex-Kent border, a memorable blizzard in 1927, and a viciously cold winter in 1929. There were some dry summers, notably 1921, the driest of the century. The decade will be remembered in Sussex for the tragedy, in 1928 , when 17 brave lifeboatmen from Rye Harbour died on a rescue mission in stormy waters.

Two determined boys take themselves and their bicycle across a flooded bridge. This is Pulborough in early January, 1925.

1920: A mild winter, but a cool, disappointing summer with some migrating birds departing early due to poor feeding conditions.

1921: The driest year of the century. Only 11.9 inches (304mm) of rain fell at Icklesham, less than 50 per cent of the annual average. October began with summer weather but a sudden downpour in Brighton led to a stampede for doorways. What appeared to be a ball of fire hovered over Market Street and instantly there was a terrific explosion which reverberated all over town. The thunder clap was followed by torrential rain.

1923: A dramatic thunderstorm which gave a pyrotechnic display of over 6,000 flashes during the night of 9th-10th July in London. Rottingdean received 4.55 inches (116mm). Hastings stayed dry.

1924: A wet year with more than 13 inches (332mm) of rain during the summer. Heavy thunderstorms broke over Midhurst on 22nd July.

1925: Following the previous year's wet weather, the winter produced a further 13.5 inches (345mm) of rain at Crawley. There was widespread flooding in the Adur Valley.

1926: A late burst of warmth in September with the mercury nudging the 80F (27C) on the 18th-19th. Dry and wet spells cancelled each other out to give an average yearly rainfall.

1927: A depression passed east along the Channel and deposited near three inches (75mm) of rain at Compton and 2.8 inches (72mm) at Patcham on 14th September. Heavy snow on Christmas night.

1929: A cold February with 144 hours of continuous frost. Only 0.02 inches (0.5mm) of rain fell in March, one of the driest months known. As if to compensate, a staggering 23.28 inches (595mm) fell in the last three months of the year - the equivalent of London's annual rainfall.

All roads lead to Rye - or do they ? The popular Rye bus, which called at most towns en route from London, has run into a snowdrift at Dunton Green, near Sevenoaks in December, 1927.

Grandad's great blizzard

Boxing Day, 1927

THE blinding, driving blizzard which began late on Christmas Day, 1927 and continued without respite for more than 36 hours is the one that most grandads will remember as "the worst snow-storm of the century, or possibly any century". Roads in Sussex were hopelessly blocked, houses were buried up to their roofs, drifts in places were 18 feet deep and villages, especially on the downs, were almost lost from sight. Grandad was not exaggerating. The great blizzard of 1927 earned its place in winter folklore before the Christmas festivities had begun to fade.

The storm was caused by a depression from the Atlantic which moved from Ireland to the English Channel and across France to the Mediterranean. It caught people on the hop. Travelling home after Christmas with relatives or friends, they ran into a raging blizzard and the whole county was littered with abandoned cars and the sight of huddled groups, trudging homewards in what had become a strange, dumb, completely white world.

It was an extraordinary climax to a year in which Lindbergh had flown the Atlantic solo, Duke Ellington had introduced a new type of dance music called jazz, Al Jolson had starred in the first "talkie" and covered-top buses had been introduced in London.

Unfortunately, the buses in Sussex were still exposed to the elements. Train passengers, too, had an uncomfortable journey. The 1.15 p.m. from Three Bridges to Tunbridge Wells ran into a huge snow-drift near East Grinstead which extended for more than a quarter of a mile. The train, which was packed, could neither proceed nor reverse and a gang of men was dispatched from East Grinstead to dig out the rear. Another engine was sent for and the train eventually returned to Three Bridges.

In Nutley six people slept all night in a car and next day took it in turns to dig themselves clear. Hotel guests along the coast were forced to extend their stay, telephone communication was impossible, shop blinds crashed under the weight of the snow and there were numerous accidents. In Chichester people went about the city as though they were going for an aeroplane trip. "It was just the motoring fraternity", said the *Evening Argus.* "They had the right garments for this weather".

The snow-plough which had been idle in Brighton Central Station since 1909 was put into action and succeeded in forcing a way through to the Dyke station followed by an army of men with shovels. There was another army of men on the Downs looking for sheep lost in snow-drifts.

The depression from the Atlantic which brought snow to Sussex, also brought heavy rain to some areas. In fact the rain was so intense that rivers quickly burst their banks and flood water rose at an alarming rate. The photograph of the bullock cart was taken at Pulborough, which always suffered on these occasions.

The crew of The Mary Stanford on the fateful day of 15th November, 1928 was led by the coxswain, Herbert Head, a 47- year-old married man. Joseph Stonham, 43, was second coxswain. The other 14 were drawn from young men of the village. Some were seamen and some fishermen and they included the three Pope brothers, Charles, Leslie and Lewis and three Cutting brothers, Henry, the bowman, Robert and Albert.. The youngest members were the Head boys, James, aged 19 and John, 17. Many of the crew were related. Photograph above shows the pall bearers on their way to the the funeral service in the small Rye Harbour community which was attended by hundreds of mourners.

The upturned boat is washed onto the shore at Rye Harbour.

Rye Harbour tragedy

15th November, 1928

IT was at 4.27 am on the stormy morning of 15th November, 1928 that the Rye Harbour Coastguard Station received a message that the Latvian steamer, *The Alice*, laden with bricks, was taking in water and drifting in the heavy seas, about three miles south-west of Dungeness.

The crew of the Rye Harbour Lifeboat, *The Mary Stanford* quickly donned their gear and rushed out, in appalling weather, to the boathouse. There was some confusion over who would make the final crew. Walter Igglesden's father at first refused to let his son go, but then relented. Lewis Pope, aged 21 was making his debut. A regular lifeboatman could not be aroused from a deep sleep. The coxswain, Herbert Head, took with him his two sons and reassured his wife about their safety.

It was a difficult launch. The tide was at its lowest, 1,000 yards from the boathouse, and the onshore wind was blowing at hurricane force. On the first two attempts to get her away, *The Mary Stanford* was blown back to shore but the exhausted launchers and oarsmen succeeded on the third attempt. At 6.45 am, the crew began the daunting task of rowing through the mountainous seas on their life-saving mission. At 6.50 am, Rye coastguards heard that the crew of *The Alice* had been rescued by a German steamer and the lifeboat's assistance was no longer required. The recall signal was fired. Men raced into the water with loud-hailers to try and stop the boat. As the weather worsened, two more Verey lights were fired. To no avail. The crew of *The Mary Stanford* was heading straight into the teeth of the gale, too late for the rescue.

At 9 am, she was seen some three miles from Dungeness with two small tug sails set and ready to turn back and head for home. At 10.30 am, a young boy on Camber Sands saw *The Mary Stanford* capsize, less than two miles from safety. His parents disbelieved his story.

The villagers had great faith in the lifeboat and their men but fears grew as the boat became over-due. Groups of relatives began to gather on the beach. At 12 noon, the boat was seen, bottom upwards, floating towards the shore. The coastguard station at Rye was informed. A maroon was fired and a hundred men, including the rocket crew, coastguards and policemen, rushed to the beach, where the upturned boat now lay.

Two men were entangled beneath the boat, but efforts to revive them proved fruitless. The tragedy unfolded slowly as, one by one, the bodies of the men were washed onto the shore. Among those on the beach was the local vicar who knelt down and prayed, surrounded by the women of the village. All the time it was raining in torrents. An eye witness said the women had run into the waves screaming as their men were washed ashore. "It was like a page from a Greek tragedy."

The close-knit community of Rye Harbour had lost an entire generation. Eleven children were left fatherless and nearly every family was affected. It was the worst single lifeboat tragedy ever known. King George V and the Prince of Wales wrote letters of sympathy. A large crowd attended the funeral on 20th November, 1928.

A memorial in the churchyard at Rye Harbour bears the words, "We have done that which was our duty to do".

With 23 degrees of frost (-13C), 15th February, 1929 was one of the coldest days Bexhill has ever known. There was, of course, a wonderful bonus. Eight successive days' skating was enjoyed by hundreds of people who flocked to Egerton Park Lake (above).

The sea was frozen for many miles along the coast in February, 1929, and so was the famous Benbow Lake at Midhurst, where skaters were in great form.

CHAPTER SIX

A glance at the thirties

IN a decade which saw the rise of Hitler and the Third Reich, growing unemployment and the Jarrow march, the death of King George V and the abdication crisis, bodyline cricket and civil war in Spain, the weather was seldom in the news. There were floods on the south coast but the gloomiest outlook of all concerned the possibility of war.

1930: A severe gale on 12th January, with winds in excess of 80 mph, felled many trees in Sussex and caused vast structural damage. In Worthing, at one time, the Lancing road was the only route out of town and scores of other roads were obstructed by fallen trees.

1932: It was a lovely August for holidaymakers with the temperature in the upper 80's F on the 19th.

1933: One of the best summers of the century. The prolonged sunshine led to the formation of dust devils in the Happy Valley, near Brighton. These fair weather vortexes are formed by the sun heating the surface layers of air. Cut grass was whirled skywards.

1934: Probably the mildest December on record. Many places failed to record a single frost.

1935: A waterspout was seen off Beachy Head on 19th July and another off Ferring on the 28th December. On 22nd December at Felbridge near East Grinstead, a number of skaters went through the ice, but they were hauled to safety by friends.

1936: A cold Easter. Cyclists, Fred Taylor and George Phillips were coastbound on Good Friday when snow began to fall. Wivelsfield was deserted and the snow lay quickly. They battled on. As they started to climb Ditchling Beacon a complete "white out" enveloped them. They managed to find shelter at the *Smugglers' Inn.*

1937: On the last day of February, blinding snow squalls swept across Sussex. At Hastings, hail fell and waves broke 50 feet high over Rock-a-Nore.

1938: Thick powdery snow fell on 18th December and the temperature fell to 25F (-4C). Along the coast, birds died of exposure and their bodies were washed up onto the beaches. Snow fell every day up to, and including, Christmas Day.

1939: A wet October and November brought 12.86 inches of rain to Crawley. Sharp frosts and snow saw out the year and acted as a foretaste of the severe weather to follow.

Buses and cars tentatively negotiate the Worthing floods on 10th November, 1931. See page 66.

The verger inspects the weather vane from the pinnacle which plunged through East Grinstead church roof on 12th January, 1930 during a heavy storm. In the same year, all four pinnacles, which were considered of an unsafe design, were rebuilt shorter than before. This work, and the repair of the damage caused to the church roof, cost the princely sum of £800.

Merrily into the mire

10th November, 1931

THERE were boats in the streets at East Worthing on Tuesday 10th November, 1931 after a heavy gale sent great waves crashing through defences. Scores of highways, including the Brighton Road, were quickly inundated and buses and cars had great difficulty finding a way through the swirling torrents. They were soon replaced by canoes.

"Planks, fishermen's stores and parts of sea defences were scattered about in profusion", said the *Worthing Gazette.* The Brighton Road was covered in shingle, basements of hotels and boarding houses were flooded and, by the evening, thousands had gathered at the sea front to see the excitement.

A few motorists, not knowing what was ahead of them, drove "merrily into the murky waters amid the cheers of onlookers. They soon changed their minds and backed away". Because of flood water on the Lancing Road, buses were diverted to a dryer route. In Rustington, vehicles were also re-routed but here it was tons of shingle which covered the road.

The gale was accompanied by heavy rain - three quarters of an inch (18.75mm) on the 9th followed by 1.5 inches (37.5mm) on the 10th. It was some of Worthing's worst weather since the great storm of 1913 which demolished the pier.

The Old Ship Inn at Winchelsea was on the beach and, inevitably, demolished by a series of storms in the twenties and thirties. It was rebuilt in its existing position inland.

Sunshine lures holiday crowds

5th, August, 1935

BRILLIANT sunshine on 5th August, 1935 lured more Britons to the Sussex coast than on any previous Bank Holiday. So many people poured into Brighton - police estimated there were 500,000 day visitors alone - that in places the shingle was invisible between their bodies.

Special trains and motor coaches were packed and, in these pre-bypass and motorway days, cars were nose to tail as they chugged through the dusty villages and towns on their way to the coast.

The nation, in 1935, was celebrating signs of increasing prosperity. Unemployment had fallen dramatically and holidays were "in vogue" again. The warmest sea water in England in August is the Channel which averages about 63F (17C) and, on this hot day in 1935, there were plenty of people prepared for a bathe.

One feature of this year was the increasing number of people using aeroplanes to reach their destination.

Deckchairs blown into the sea

16th September, 1935

A sou'wester gale accompanied by heavy, driving rain and an exceptionally high tide hit the South Coast on 16th and 17th September, 1935, swept away bathing huts at Bognor Regis and reduced them to floating piles of driftwood.

"Some were wrenched off bodily and carried out to sea, tossing like corks on the breakers", said the *Sussex Daily News*. A number of deck chairs were also blown into the sea and when the tide ebbed, the foreshore, near the pier, was strewn with wreckage.

At Worthing, an itinerant sleeping rough was tugged out to sea and was drowned. Selsey Bill lost 30 feet of its cliffs.The electric train service between Newhaven and Seaford was halted. An earth embankment at Hove was washed away and a two-mile stretch littered with "beach, sand and seaweed". At Brighton, boats and canoes were lifted on to the promenade and tons of shingle hurled into the amusement arcades. An elderly resident said: " The noise made by the dislodged slates sounded like a machine-gun barrage".

It took many months to restore the sea wall at Hove, where tons of rubble had to be tipped, leading eventually to the building of the present promenade.

Late February, 1937. The Brighton and Hove Herald van became stuck in a snowdrift as the intrepid reporter went in search of snow stories.

River Ouse laps into Lewes

November, 1935

THE Ouse is the second largest river in Sussex and is 39 miles long, including a tidal length, from Barcombe to Newhaven, of 13 miles. It rises at Slaugham from the springs of the Tunbridge Wells some 300 feet above sea level and cuts through the escarpment of the South Downs at Lewes. In this narrow, steep sided valley town, just above the coastal flood plain, the tidal waters of the Ouse have frequently overtopped the defences and flooded the lower-lying land.

In November, 1935 torrential rain cascaded from the downs and joined the swirling torrents of the swollen Ouse which once again invaded Lewes. The photograph, on the right, appeared in the Herald Magazine on 23rd November. It shows Winterbourne Hollow under water after a high wall had collapsed in St. Pancras Gardens. The inhabitants of Lewes suffered greatly.

On the left of the photograph is the caretaker of the Pells Baths, and his wife, leaving their flooded home. The other pictures were taken in Southover area.

Photographs of the Lewes floods in The Herald Magazine on 22nd November, 1935.

Wartime defences on the Dungeness Peninsular at Walland Marsh.

War postponed by ice

December, 1939 - February, 1940

24th January, 1940 and Plummers offers winter bargains in the Eastbourne Gazette, thus breaking the two-week censorship on all weather news.

SUSSEX was buried in a blanket of snow, but it was a secret ! This was the strange scenario in the early weeks of 1940 when all references to the weather were censored for 15 days for fear the information could be useful to the enemy. It didn't really matter. The whole of Europe, even Portugal and Spain, was held in the icy grip of one of the severest frosts on record.

If Hitler had invaded Sussex he would have needed plenty of shovels. Towns and villages were cut off, supplies of fuel were dangerously low and a piercing north-east wind blew for several weeks. So Adolf stayed at home and, for a while, the war was postponed.

The Great Frost extended unbroken, apart from two short thaws, from 22nd December, 1939 to 4th February, 1940. At Slinfold in West Sussex on 29th December, a reading of just 2F (-16C) was registered by the grass thermometer. Bodiam went even lower. The quick-silver retreated almost to the bulb where -4F (-21.1C) was registered in the air. It was the lowest authenticated Sussex reading.

It was not long before mild Atlantic air edged in to do battle with the cold heavyweight air. What followed, on the night of 27th January, was a spectacular ice-storm, or glaze. Heavy rain of a super-cooled variety fell and all objects it touched were immediately encased in a film of ice. Pieces of grass appeared as glass rods, telephone wires, carrying 80-90 lbs of ice, either snapped or sank to the ground. Birds were frozen by their feet to branches of trees where they had roosted the previous night. In Maresfield, fantail pigeons were fixed to the roof of a house. Rooks fell from trees with their wings welded together and live sheep were frozen by

Milk roundsmen abandoned their wheeled prams and carried on deliveries with sledges. This is Eastbourne in January, 1940.

their wool to gorse bushes on the South Downs.

During those bitterly cold weeks a total of 29 ground frosts were recorded and this resulted in the rare spectacle of frozen sea off the South coast. Many shallow waters were fringed or covered with ice, especially in shallow creeks or harbours such as Bosham, Chichester, Emsworth and Langstone.

Like other Sussex towns, Eastbourne had to wait for 15 days for the full story, but the *Gazette* then reported: "Its lateness does not mean it is stale news. It has, in fact, been the principal topic of conversation ever since the grey, forbidding skies released their store of snow silently and relentlessly from dusk to past midnight.

"Some remarkable sights were witnessed. Milk roundsmen abandoned their wheeled prams and carried on their deliveries with sledges. The same mode of conveyance was adopted by errand boys.

Winter sports claimed many enthusiasts and there was a daily trek to The Downs and to Paradise. In level places the snow covered the ground to a depth of 18 inches. In drifts it was as deep as six feet. Seagulls were frozen to death when they became trapped on the ice."

In Horsham, controversy arose over who should be employed for snow-clearing work. A ratepayer wrote to the *West Sussex County Times*: "Bricklayers, carpenters, plasterers and painters are employed as snow sweepers while the unemployed still stand in the queue at Brighton Road".

The thaw eventually arrived in early February with heavy rain but this was short-lived. The frost returned on 10th February and, on the night of the 13th, produced 21.5 degrees of frost (-12C). For Sussex it was the coldest winter since 1895.

CHAPTER SIX

The war years and beyond

Dominated by the Great Frosts of 1940 and 1947, and the hardships they caused, this decade will be remembered also for summer storms and some long, balmy days of sunshine - and drought. The photograph, on page 81, of the ladies of Peacehaven queuing for water, says something about the patience and resilience of the people of the "front-line" county of Sussex. After all the conflicts of the previous eight years, this was almost the last straw.

1940, 1941 and 1942: The first three winters of the war were all cold and snowy. In 1941, Hastings had 21 days when snow covered the ground.

1943: Charles II's conception of an English summer - "three fine days and a thunderstorm" - was applicable to this year, for the last week in July brought a short, hot spell with temperatures up to 88F (31C). This ended abruptly on the 31st with thunderstorms and squally winds.

1944: Britain's hottest ever May day took place on the 29th at Horsham when the mercury shot up to 91F (32.8C).

1945: A severe gale on 18th-19th January ushered in a wintry spell. Worthing saw snow on the ground for 15 days during this month.

1946: As in 1938, a cold spell developed in the middle of December and there was talk of another White Christmas. It was not to be. The weather changed and the festive season was mild. The year of 1946 was wet with more than 40 inches (1000mm) of rain in places.

1946: A whirlwind visited the village of Fairlight, near Hastings on 4th July and caused considerable damage around the church, high on the hilltop. Chimney stacks were blown down, a barn was demolished and numerous slates and tiles removed. Rainfall was torrential and at Clive Vale 1.36 inches (35mm) fell - most of it in just two hours after midnight. Observers from Eastbourne were treated to a grand spectacle of lightning which appeared to strike the sea.

1947: A sensational weather year with the coldest February of the century, the wettest March, a warm, and at times, hot summer and an August drought that continued into October. There were one or two blights on the salad days such as a severe thunderstorm at Hastings on 17th July which gave two inches (49mm) of rain. An intrepid trip to New Zealand which began on Christmas Day, by Mr H.C.Johnson, skipper of the 37-ton yawl, *The Nebula* carrying eight passengers was foiled by a gale which drove the boat aground near Southden Estate, Middleton only two days out of Shoreham Harbour. The crew of the Selsey lifeboat went to the rescue in terrible weather and took the distressed adventurers to Littlehampton.

1948: In what was a mild winter, a short but harsh taste of Arctic cold swept snow from the east on 20th February and, as the sky cleared, the temperature dropped to just 8F (-13C) at Hurstpierpoint. An observer filled a 1lb jam jar with water and placed it on the snow surface where the temperature was -1F (-19C). It froze almost immediately. July produced an equally short but notable event, a heatwave on the last few days with more than 90F (32C).

1949: A dry year which heralded its intentions by displaying the warmest Easter on record. Nearly every month had below average rainfall, culminating in restrictions by September. At East Grinstead, a "save-water" appeal was broadcast at the town's carnival. At Brighton, the dry weather led to the death of an elderly couple when a large branch from a beech tree fell on to them at Patcham Place. The rains returned in October with a vengeance, giving 8.5 inches (218 mm) by the end of the month.

The sunshine recorder worked overtime at Eastbourne, measuring 2,153 hours of sun, or nearly six hours a day averaged throughout the year.

The Soviet steamer, Ussuri (2,498 tons) aground on Seaford beach after losing her way in dense fog. The ship ploughed through a wooden breaker and bumped into the concrete promenade. Crowds of people flocked to the beach to see her.

Clear blue skies for Battle of Britain

June - October, 1940

THE weather had played its part in postponing the war at the beginning of 1940; now with the RAF squadrons ready for battle it was to have a crucial role in the hectic days of aerial combat which lay ahead.

Close to Chichester and the sea was the premier defence establishment in Sussex. RAF Tangmere, a Sector A station, was home to four fighter squadrons at the beginning of July, all of them flying Hurricanes. During this month they were involved in regular skirmishes with the Luftwaffe over the Channel resulting in numerous successes and, inevitably, some losses. The weather was variable with a few dirty days of fog, low cloud and intermittent summer rain. Many young pilots were briefed for a sortie and then, after one look at the weather reports, drank an early morning cup of tea and returned for a lie-in.

The July weather improved dramatically. Scudding clouds thinned to reveal rapidly growing patches of blue and the great aerial battles began in earnest with the Luftwaffe keen to wipe Tangmere off of the map as a preliminary to the invasion of Britain. They waited until the weather was perfect and on

16th August, a large force of Junkers dive bombers screamed out of the sun in a devastating attack on the airfield. It left many dead and injured, with two hangars destroyed and numerous other buildings damaged. Six Blenheims, seven Hurricanes, one Magister and one Spitfire were destroyed.

Somehow Tangmere continued to be operational and went through the remainder of the Battle of Britain in the forefront of Britain's defence. During the brilliant clear days of the first week of September, when the barometer remained high and the skies were almost always blue, the Tangmere pilots were in constant action. Day after day, cocooned in their cockpits, they climbed into the rising thermals from a sun-baked earth, striving for precious height. Eventually the Luftwaffe threat was repulsed. The Germans returned to their bases leaving a parched Sussex countryside littered with the smoking wrecks of aircraft.

The battle raged on through the autumnal days of October until Hitler postponed his proposed invasion of Britain.

Storm harvest for Hastings

22nd - 26th October, 1945

THIS was the fisherman's storm. After a Channel gale had raged for four consecutive days, leaving south coast resorts bruised and battered once again, there was one great bonus. Large shoals of fish, particularly mackerel, were driven close to the shore by the agitated sea and when the weather had abated, hundreds of fishermen were able to reap the rewards of a wonderful harvest.

For the landlubbers there was no such joy. Winds in excess of 70 miles an hour swept through the county like a tornado. In Hastings, tiles and slates were stripped from houses, windows caved in and, according to the *Hastings Observer,* dustbin lids just sailed away. In Elphinstone Road, Hastings, the wind demolished a chimney which fell against the chimney of the next door house. Both then crashed through the roof of No 29, killing an 80-year-old woman as she lay in bed.

In the early afternoon of Friday 26th October, hundreds of people braved the winds to take part in the seasonal Hastings sport of wave-watching. Huge mountains of spray broke over the promenade and rushed into the town centre which was soon under water. Many shoppers were trapped and a boat was used to ferry people across the road at the deepest points. One woman who was buying fish for her husband's dinner was unable to reach the shop. She turned back when a rush of water nearly knocked her off her feet. Looking down she saw, floundering in the flood, a good-sized bass. The woman picked up the live fish, put it in her shopping bag and waded home !

At West St Leonards a mine was found stranded on the beach near the Bathing Pool. Naval experts successfully removed the detonators and the mine was triumphantly hauled up the beach.

Huge mountains of spray broke over the promenade and rushed into Hastings town centre.

Dangerous waters

9th January, 1946

THE war was over by many months but the dangerously mined waters of Sussex still posed a great threat to all who put to sea, especially in stormy weather. The early days of January, 1946 provided a succession of scares. A sea mine which was washed ashore at Seaford during a violent gale on Wednesday 9th January lay right in the middle of the esplanade opposite the Salts recreation ground. An anti-mine squad who rendered it harmless, spotted another but this drifted away beyond Seaford Head.

During that night the sea wall took another pounding from moutainous waves, widening and lengthening the damage near the Buckle Road. Three cars with engines swamped by sea water were abandoned near the Buckle Inn and other motorists travelling westwards were diverted through East Blatchington.

The next morning three mines were reported off Peacehaven and, in the afternoon, one of them exploded so violently that it was felt as far away as Seaford. Houses and shops were damaged by the force of the detonation and, as night-time came, many people waited for further explosions . The mines were last seen drifting away into the darkness.

Splash Point Hotel, originally a private house, was once a focal point close to the summit of Seaford Head. The regular erosion of the cliffs so undermined the road leading to the hotel that it had to be demolished after the war for fear it would slip into the sea.

Diary of a bleak, hard winter

January - March, 1947

BY the third week in January, 1947 the people of Sussex were confident they had escaped any tricks the weather might have in store. Although food and fuel was still scarce, and in many poorer homes people used broken furniture to keep the embers glowing, there was no sign of snow. However, on 23rd January, the wind swung to the east and winter arrived with a vengeance - a winter of blizzards, sub-zero temperatures, endless grey skies and great hardships. Here is a Sussex diary of the notoriously bleak winter of 1947.

23rd January: Temperature drops to 31F (-0C) at Rotherfield. Snow settles at Preston Park, Brighton.

26th January: AA reports that most roads in East Sussex are impassable "without chains". Harting Hills, near Midhurst out of bounds for Southdown buses.

27th January: Snowploughs in Crowborough after six successive days of snow. Many power cuts throughout county. Eleven people treated at Worthing for broken bones. Maximum temperature at Worthing is 28F (-2C),

28th January: A new blizzard rages and buses are withdrawn at Hastings. Temperature at Hove falls to 17F (-8C), the coldest reading for 19 years. Bus skids into a ditch at Littlehampton. Rye is cut off at Winchelsea Hill and roundsmen use a sledge at East Grinstead.

29th January: Threat of power cuts. Sea is frozen at Folkestone. German POW's help to clear the snow in Lewes and Horsham. Ski-ing on the Downs above Eastbourne. A night temperature of 10F (-12C) at Capel Green, Crowborough.

30th January: Mercury falls to 8F (-13C) at Tunbridge Wells. Major gas and electricity cuts. Food is rationed. Thousands of frozen pipes in Brighton. Sussex schools shut but "open for milk" in Brighton. National Fire Service delivers 500 gallons of water daily. Army is engaged on the Chichester Road to clear snow. Pensioners at Worthing and St Leonards die after sweeping snow.

31st January: The whole of Sussex is icebound. More snow at Tangmere. First in eight days when temperature exceeds freezing at Haywards Heath.

3rd February: Bognor reaches 39F (4C) and begins to thaw. Telephone cables flooded at Brighton. Thousands of burst pipes at Bognor.

6th February: Two boys die after falling through the ice at Crowborough. Below freezing again at Eastbourne, Worthing and Tunbridge Wells. Clearing up continues on railway landslide between Wadhurst and Ticehurst.

9th February: The Collier, *Quaysider*, unloads coal at Shoreham Harbour after a trip from Grangemouth which takes eight days instead of two.

11th - 14th February: Coal crisis worsens. Brighton's trolleybus service cut. Nearly two million idle by enforced cuts in UK factories. Many blackouts in Sussex. So many accidents on the ice that police cars are used as ambulances.

21st February: Dull, heavy snow again. Nine inches fall in Horsham. Trolleybuses in Brighton halted. Up to 200 people a day turned away from coalmerchants in Brighton.

23rd February: Brilliant sunshine after 21 days without. Scenes like Switzerland at South Coast resorts. Temperatures fall to 17F (-8C) at Littlehampton. 200 skiers and tobogganers take to the hills at Eastbourne.

24th February: One of the coldest dawns of the 20th century. Tunbridge Wells min. 4F (-16C), Eastbourne 15F (-9C), Horsham 1F (-17C), Worthing 18F (-8C), Littlehampton 14F (-10C) and Bognor Regis 19F (-7C). Part of the English Channel frozen for several miles. At Crawley Down, spray freezes on firemen's tunics.

4th March: On the eve of a promised thaw, a blizzard with 60 mph winds tears across Southern England. Brighton train takes eight hours to get to London. Telephone lines down in Brighton. An ice storm of freezing rain welds a car to the ground at Gatwick and icicles hang from people's hats at East Grinstead.

5th March: Telegraph poles snap under weight of ice at Hastings. Worst travelling period "in living memory". Rain freezes on trees turning them "into crystalline stalactites", near Horsham.

Many miles of telephone wires came down under the weight of frozen rain which turned to ice. This picture was taken at Marshlands Farm, Heathfield in early March, 1947.

9th - 12th March: Temperature rises to 48F (9C) at Littlehampton and promenaders are out in great numbers. This is followed by a great deluge. Three feet of floodwater near Petworth, hundreds of acres of Pulborough flooded, roads impassable at Wisborough Green. Coal fuels still dangerously low.

13th - 17th March: Snow, rain, floods and gale-force winds. Visibility 200 yards on the Lewes Road in blinding blizzard. Floods at Barcombe mills. Trees uprooted with extensive structural damage. Housewives wade through floodwater at Lancing on their way to the village shops. Temperature at Eastbourne is 50F (10C).

27th March: The winter of 1947 has its final fling. Heavy sleet and snow falls in Brighton and Lewes but quickly melts.

Council workmen had a thankless task in 1947 in clearing frozen snow from the town centre in Shoreham.

Ice and fire at Nymans

February, 1947

THE beautiful Elizabethan mansion of Nymans at Handcross was destroyed by fire during a week in which some of the coldest weather of the century occurred.

At 3am on Wednesday 19th February, 1947, Lieutenant Colonel L.C.R.Messel, aged 75, former High Sherriff of Sussex, was awakened by the smell of burning. He raised the alarm and roused his wife and eight other occupants who were able to escape from the burning house into the snow-covered grounds, even though they had no time to dress. On that frosty night - the temperature at around 25F (-4C) - flames leapt 30 feet into the night sky and Haywards Heath firemen could see them as they set out along the icy roads to the scene.

National Fire Service crews from 10 stations across Sussex battled against the blaze, and water from their hoses froze on the exterior of the mansion,

causing large icicles to festoon the building.

Treasures worth thousands of pounds were ruined in the fire as the Messels sheltered in a stable block nearby. Efforts were made to salvage furniture, and blackened valuables, antiques and other items were piled up in the snow-covered garden. When firemen eventually put out the flames they were unable to roll up the hoses which had frozen stiff.

A similar situation occurred at Crawley Down in the small hours of Monday 24th February, 1947 - in some places the coldest night of the century, with temperatures down to 1F (-17C) north of Gatwick. As East Grinstead firemen fought a fire at Crawley Down Garage, ice formed on their faces, hands and clothing, hampering their operation.

A contemporary account quoted a fireman as saying: "In a few moments we turned into ice men."

A double-decker Southdown bus was blown over by a mighty gust of wind as it was crossing the Old Shoreham bridge on 7th January, 1949 in chaotic conditions. The bus, full of passengers, crashed into a half-submerged sandbank and rolled onto its side. There was a low tide at the time and, miraculously, no-one was drowned, or died from their injuries. Those involved in this amazing accident long remembered the heroic efforts of a nearby resident, Mrs Winifred Firthkettle who quickly provided a ladder to help the trapped passengers escape from the bus.

When Peacehaven ran dry

Peacehaven is a settlement on top of the cliffs of the South Downs. It was created as a dream development of cheap housing after the 1914-18 war on a stretch of downland above the warm waters of the English Channel. In a literal sense it is far from a peaceful haven for there is nowhere for vessels in distress to find refuge and there are few scraps of comfort for the inhabitants when the Sussex weather misbehaves.

It was heat, not storms, which caused tempers to fray in Peacehaven in the summer of 1949. Day after day, throughout June, July and August, the sun bore down onto a parched earth, straining the resources of the fire service. Heathland and forest fires were widespread, rivers ran dry and water was strictly rationed.

The photograph was taken on 14th September in Roderick Avenue, Peacehaven where large tanks were filled daily with drinking water for housewives to draw. For several weeks in this extraordinary summer they walked to the site with buckets, bottles, jugs and even kettles and then waited patiently for their turn to draw their ration.

CHAPTER EIGHT

Sussex weather in the fifties

A decade in which acres of Selsey Bill slipped into the sea, and there was more than a fair share of ferocious storms and blizzards. Two years, however, stand out. In 1956 there was severe cold in February, a drought in May, fierce gales in July, hailstorms in August and, as a festive finale, snow on Christmas night. In 1958, a storm in Horsham earned a place in meteorological history for the size of the hailstones that fell.

1950: A secondary depression moved east-south-east across southern England during the early hours of 26th April and, in the polar air in its wake, heavy snow fell. Up to six inches covered the ground between Fernhurst and Crawley.

1951: One of the wettest years known. At South Harting, 57.21 inches (1,464 mm) fell. Unusually, February was one of the wettest months of the year in some parts of north Sussex.

1952: Snow fell across Sussex between 27th and 30th March with day temperatures on the 29th remaining below freezing, the latest widespsread occurrence known. At East Grinstead, bus services to Saints Hill were withdrawn for two days because of snow drifts.

1953: On 31st January, a storm surge, driven by hurricane-force north-westerly winds, crashed against the east coast sea defences, causing widespsread flooding and extensive damage to more than 1,000 miles of coastline. In parts of Kent, Essex and East Anglia, it was the most catastrophic event of the century with many lives lost, but Sussex and the South Coast escaped almost completely.

1954: A severe cold spell in early February froze two swans into the ice at Woolborough Farm, North Gate, Crawley. Workmen had to break ice several inches thick to free them.
More than 4.5 inches (112.5mm) of rain fell during the last week in November accompanied by strong winds which blew down a number of trees.

1955: On the 18th May, it began sunny, rained at lunch time, then snow fell during the afternoon. High winds brought down the banners bedecking the High Street for the Crawley Festival.

1957: As in 1951, February was the wettest month of the year with 5.5 inches (137.5mm) of rain, but only a meagre 0.2 inches(5mm) fell in April. In June, Littlehampton recorded 339 hours of sunshine, an average of more than 11 hours per day.

A little girl sweeps away ice with her broom. This is Tunbridge Wells on August Bank Holiday Monday, 1956.

1958: A cold Easter with snow lying on Easter Saturday (5th April). Due to the severe thunderstorms which tracked across Sussex, Surrey and Kent on the evening of 5th September, flooding and landslips prevented many boat trains from reaching Dover or Folkestone and ferries switched to Newhaven. More than 12,000 passengers passed through the port on Saturday 6th September, four times the normal volume.

1959: February was rainless in parts of East Sussex. During the period 14th August to 9th October only 0.19 inches (5 mm) fell at Crawley. The fine weather meant a boom at the Black Rock Baths in Brighton which averaged nearly 3,000 bathers each Sunday during the summer.

An unpleasant scene in a pleasant town. High winds in February, 1951 brought down this tree onto a house in Church Street, Petworth. Photograph shows firemen and onlookers inspecting the damage in pouring rain.

December, 1951 and the sea front at Worthing was littered with boats tossed from the beach by the waves.

Picking up the pieces. Inhabitants of Selsey survey the damage after the December storm,1951.

Selsey under the sea

A prolonged spell of violent gales with winds in excess of 80 miles-an-hour roared across the English Channel in late December, 1951 causing grievous damage yet again to the battle-weary promontory of Selsey.

It was on the night of 28th December that the sea broke through the shingle bank and flowed inland to the town itself. East Beach was washed away and bungalows in Manor Lane were flooded to a depth of three to four feet. Soaked to the skin, the inhabitants were evacuated and spent the night in Selsey Hotel. Electricity supplies were cut and part of Broadreeds Camp destroyed.

All the way along the Sussex coast, seaside paraphernalia and promenades were attacked and the recently installed defences at Littlehampton, Seaford and Pett Level, which had cost many thousands of pounds, had an immense battering. They held firm, leaving the people of Selsey alone with the fears that, one day, the community would be at the bottom of the sea. For them there was little comfort in the knowledge that the sea-bed, nearly out to The Owers, is covered with the ruins of earlier Selseys.

The Sussex Magazine, commenting on the storm of 1951 said: "Regardless of the known facts people continue to live on sites in Selsey which are sure to be threatened again and again. As long as the English weather and the Channel remain unchanged, human efforts will not amount to much against them; the sea's toll of Sussex is an ever-recurring Danegeld !"

In 1952 a report on coast erosion indicated that Selsey had lost more land for every yard of frontage than any other place in the British Isles and it was proposed that £200,000 be spent on defence, a conservative figure even in 1952. Although 20 feet of beach was being lost to the sea every year, the people who had made their home in this beautiful, but often inhospitable, part of West Sussex had no intention of leaving.

Today, the local fishermen at Selsey still talk about fishing "in the park". By that they mean the park of the Bishops which lies many fathoms deep, some way out to sea. Also submerged is the site of Selsey's old Saxon Cathedral, washed away by the Sussex storms.

Lamb before the lion

March, 1952

MARCH is said to come in like a lion and go out like a lamb. In 1952 the reverse happened. The month began with temperatures climbing towards 60F (16C) with a breeze that hardly ruffled the feathers. As the month neared an end, the wind changed to the East and North East and bitterly cold air brought temperatures tumbling.

By 28th March the mercury reached just 38F (3C) at Tunbridge Wells and 40F (4C) at Eastbourne. The forecast was grim. Strong winds, snow showers, frost at night. Sussex was facing its coldest late March since 1916.

Saturday 29th March was a day of blizzards and roads were quickly blocked. Icy conditions prevailed at Hove, Bexhill, Hastings and the hills around Tunbridge Wells. Several inches of snow lay across Sussex and, at Littlehampton, the heavy sleet which lay in the area was equivalent to 16mm of rain. It was the worst spell of weather since 1947 and 70 roads in the county were blocked by snow.

At East Grinstead, a plough went to the aid of cars marooned in a 400-yard stretch of Imberhorne Lane, where the drifts were three feet deep. There was a similar story at Beachgreen Lane, Blackham, where two cars and a van could "not force a passage". Ploughs were at work in Selsfield, West Hoathly and Tyne Cross. Roads across Ashdown Forest were cut off. At Beachy Head, the conditions were atrocious and seven ships had to wait off Seaford and Newhaven for the weather to relent.

On Monday 31st March conditions improved sufficiently for the sun to melt the drifts. There were some night frosts in early April but by the 9th the temperatures in Sussex had reached almost 70F (21C). It was like moving from January to July in just a few days !

Anyone leaving a car close to the sea wall at Seaford, in stormy weather, is really asking for trouble. When the driver of this car returned, he found his vehicle buried and battered by shingle and larger boulders. This was taken in December, 1954.

Heavy snow fell in Hampshire, Dorset and many parts of West Sussex on 27th January, 1954.
It extended as far east as Haslemere and Chichester, where snow fell all day and was more
than 12 inches deep by evening. A few miles to the east no snow fell at all as the frontal cloud
did not extend that far . The photograph above was taken at Haslemere station as a postman
waited patiently on the platform, wondering if the London train would make it from
Southampton.

The heavy snow of January, 1954 and a car carefully negotiates a way through the drifts at Chilgrove Hill, near Chichester.

The front page of the Chichester Observer on Friday 13th January, 1956, after a five-minute tornado had ripped through the village of Sidlesham, blowing down trees and buildings and smashing glasshouses to pieces. One woman said : "It was like aeroplanes flying about the house. Everything moved at once. The carpets flapped on the floors, the tiles came tumbling off the roof and coping stones were torn away."

Chichester and Observer

FRIDAY,

.ng
ONS IN & MILLINERY
HING FABRICS ..EARING PRICES
SOUTH ST., CHICHESTER

No. 4,259   Registered at the General Post Office as a Newspaper.   LARGEST SALES OF ANY

Scenes Of Havoc Left By Five-Minute Tornado

VIOLENT STORM HITS SIDLESHAM

TEACHERS ARE CONFIDENT

Chichester and Associa-

Smallholders Have Their Crops, Property Wrecked

July gale and August hail

29th July - 6th August, 1956

THE year 1956 had already earned a place in weather's hall of fame for the extreme cold of February. This was reinforced by a dry spring which led to water restrictions and, ironically, to those who lived on the south coast in sight of limitless sea water, a ban on hoses and sprinklers.

June was dull and July unsettled and the people of Sussex were looking forward, almost desperately, for some sign of summer. It was not to be. At the end of July an intense area of low pressure brought a fierce storm with winds that gusted to more than 85 mph at Brighton - most unusual for a summer month. Death and destruction followed on such a scale it was difficult to believe this was July. On Sunday morning, the 29th, the wind did not drop below storm force for two hours. It was compared, somewhat romantically, with the tempest which scattered the Spanish Armada in 1588.

There was nothing romantic for holidaymakers at Brighton's Sheepcote Valley camping ground, where scores of tents were blown down and ripped to shreds. Many had just arrived and their belongings were scattered across the hillside with pieces of canvas flapping forlornly in the hedges.

In a field at Cakeham Tower, West Wittering, a tree toppled onto a party of campers, killing a woman. At Handcross, a van driver had to stop to avoid a fallen tree which obstructed the road. As he was gingerly trying to avoid the obstacle, another tree fell on the van and he was killed. In the village, electricity cables were severed. Salt spray was whipped up and blown many miles inland. On its way it seared and blackened 40,000 plants on Brighton seafront. In Stanmer Park, 300 trees were blown down.

There was chaos all along the Sussex coast. A giant marquee erected for an orchestral concert was just a tattered wooden skeleton and 750 deckchairs were picked up and dumped in the sea. At The Quadrant, Goring, the side wall of a house collapsed and part of the roof blew away. Littlehampton lost 70 beach huts and the Shoreham Lifeboat was called out seven times in five days, including three times on the Sunday. It was the busiest time in the Lifeboat's history.

To be out in the streets walking into the teeth of this gale would have sapped the strength of the toughest individual. A 90-year-old lady defiantly strode through Hove on her way to church but violent gusts flung her down a flight of steps and she died from her injuries.

In the mountainous seas of the Channel, a yachtsman fell overboard but somehow managed to haul himself aboard after a considerable buffeting by the churning sea. The vessel was taking part in a cross-Channel race from Southsea. The seven-man crew made a dash for a safe haven but the sea held them in its grip for six terrifying hours. Finally the boat capsized offshore at Bognor and, as they clung to the yacht, around 50 people braved the breakers to affect a rescue from the beach.

Ice survives for days in high summer

6th August, 1956

THE July gales had hardly died down when this appalling summer took another turn for the worse. Hail, bigger than walnuts, and lying as deep as a winter snowstorm was to blight the August Bank Holiday.

The 6th August was cool and especially so at high levels in the atmosphere. Huge cumulo-nimbus clouds had built up by mid-morning and strong up-draughts within them carried particles of ice even higher, growing larger all the time. Finally the air currents could hold their icy load no longer. Rain and hail cascaded down.

As so often happens during atmospherically unstable conditions, some places continued to bathe in sunshine. Holidaymakers at Brighton and Eastbourne were enjoying the summer while at Arundel, roofs were collapsing under the weight of the hail. At Arundel Castle, 1.7 inches (46mm) of rain and melted hail fell in just 18 minutes.

The main Brighton to Portsmouth Road was blocked as a two-foot deep layer of hail covered Arundel's Old Market Square, causing a two-mile traffic queue. Two houses in Maltravers Street caved in under the weight of hail. Firemen pumped out flooded properties and crops were flattened.

Several days later, a visitor to Arundel wondered what the black substance was that lined the grass verge by the Castle boating lake. It was one foot of hail which had been swept off the road by council workmen. It was black and had been shaded by trees. It had, however, survived several days in high summer in the South of England !

An extraordinary scene in the centre of Arundel on August Bank Holiday, 1956. A two-feet deep layer of hail covers the road after the equivalent of 1.7 inches fell in just 18 minutes.

An attempt is made to clear the ice from the centre of Tunbridge Wells.

Ice storm on an August day

August Monday, 1956

THE scene in Tunbridge Wells and the Sussex border villages on August Bank Holiday morning, 1956 was quite astounding. A storm had unleashed so many hailstones that they formed a moving icy mass, which, said an eye witness, "looked like rice pudding on an unimaginable scale".

The storm began in the middle of the morning on 6th August with thunder and lightning, followed by heavy rain, and then hail. At first the hailstones were small but just before mid-day they shot down from the sky as big as cherries, smashing windows and skylights and tearing blinds to shreds.

The hailstones made a white carpet in Tunbridge Wells and was swept into great drifts by The Pantiles. While local residents rolled up their trouser legs and tried to clear the blocked drains, two young people were in the middle of an adventure they will never forget.

John Rogers and his friend Richard were climbing on nearby Harrison's Rocks when the hail began to fall. "Not legendary tennis balls", said John, "just ordinary hailstones, but the duration was extraordinary. They kept on falling. They covered the ground and began to pile up. I was stuck on the cliff face with the rope frozen into a crevice above me. I abseiled down, recovered the rope and walked into town.

"The scene in the centre of Tunbridge Wells was incredible. In the area around The Pantiles, the hailsnow was several feet deep. People said it had avalanched off the Common. That hardly seemed likely, but how else to account for the depth covering the area ? I had a camera with me and took some pictures."

John Rogers took these amazing photographs with a Brownie camera in the centre of Tunbridge Wells on 6th August, 1956 after the incredible hailstorm. They capture the clean-up exercise in progress, from the municipal bulldozer doing service as a snow plough to the policeman with a shovel. John sold his pictures to the Daily Mail for the handsome sum of £15. Three years later he received a demand for unpaid tax !

BARCOMBE CRICKET PAVILION

AND RECREATION GROUND

AFTER
THE GREAT HAILSTORM
6th August (Bank Holiday) 1956.

Charles Seagar, a member of Barcombe Cricket Club, took these pictures at 3.15 pm on August Bank Holiday after the great hailstorm had caused play to be abandoned for the day. The pavilion looks as if it is covered by snow and the stumps are surrounded by hail that is ankle deep. How many times has ice stopped play in Britain in August ?

The largest hailstones ever

5th September, 1958

GIANT hailstones, as large as tennis balls, vivid flashes of lightning and a devastating wind. The evening of 5th September, 1958 would be forever etched on the memories of those who lived in and around a swathe of Sussex from Horsham, through Crawley and across to East Grinstead.

Those who ventured out into the streets fled in terror as monster-sized hail dented even sturdy motorcars, smashed thousands of panes of glass and injured several people. One woman was almost knocked unconscious by the hail as she attempted to rescue her pet rabbit from the garden.

The storm was a self-perpetuating travelling variety, a super cell, the type that has the mechanics to manufacture enormous hail, especially at its onset and the ability to spawn a tornado - a violent whirling vortex of air, generating speeds well in excess of hurricane force. A tornado accompanied this September storm in north-west Sussex.

First reports of something extraordinary came in from Pulborough where the Codmere Hill nurseries lost more than 13,000 panes of glass. The noise was earsplitting and the nursery forewoman said it sounded like a machine-gun attack. Further north, at Bucks Green, it looked as if a giant lawnmower had driven right across the fields. Acres of crops were unrecognisable. A fruit farm at Wisborough Green lost 90 per cent of its apples and pears. One farmer had 90 acres of corn flattened. Heavy rain fell as well and even silenced the organ at Wisborough Parish Church when floodwater jammed the stops.

As the storm moved north-east the hail grew even larger and the tornado was spawned. At Southwater, a garage was left with only its walls standing. Parts of the roof were carried a quarter of a mile, knocking down electricity cables and a letter box on the way. The garage proprietor clambered out of the wreckage along with his assistant. They were unhurt. Meanwhile, hail the size of pullet's eggs was falling. Some hailstones were bigger than tennis balls. They weighed nearly half a pound, tore bark off trees and pitted the ground to several inches in depth. They were the largest ever to have fallen in Britain.

The storm pulled out whole trees by the roots. Others were twisted and contorted. Cottages were wrecked, as if clasped and wrung by a giant hand. Mrs Winifred Bromley was alone in Yew Tree Cottage along the Crawley to Horsham Road when the door was flung open and a mass of debris was swept into the room pinning her against the wall and injuring her arm. Chimneys collapsed, windows burst open

and a sheet of corrugated iron was wrapped around a tree.

In Queen Street, Horsham, an eye witness dashed for cover in the lee of buildings. "The air seemd to be a solid mass of rain, hail and a crushing wind", he said. "Wreckage was being swept through the gaps in buildings." At Horsham Football ground, the 100-foot timber roof was peeled back and levitated towards houses on Queen's Way. A large oak tree arrested its progress before impact.

In the Horsham rural district, 550 council homes suffered roof and window damage with Billingshurst, Broadbridge Heath and Slinfold the worst affected. There were at least one thousand mangled telephone lines to repair.

The storm continued on its path of destruction, skirting Crawley. At Ifield there was mayhem. In a narrow belt from the golf course to Gatwick Airport, 700 trees either crashed down or were beheaded and twisted out of recognition. Five boys had a lucky escape at Ifield Hall, a Dr Barnado's Home. The boys made a field kitchen of corrugated iron in the grounds which collapsed on top of them. They managed to scramble out.

In Bonnett's Lane, Maxey Cottage was hit by falling trees and telegraph poles and struck by lightning. The occupants were at the Brighton Show, blissfully unaware of the havoc being wreaked at their home. More than 50 trees fell in this lane alone.

At Gatwick Airport, a squall ripped off the roof of the Transair building. A gust of 80 mph was registered. All aircraft were grounded early but passengers on an incoming flight by Jersey Airlines found the journey a little hazardous. Captain Newman said: "It was pitch black and we were violently thrown about." The aircraft, with 15 passengers, landed safely but with serious damage to the engine cowling which was pitted by hail. A Dakota was lifted off the ground and hurled several yards across the tarmac.

The storm had now reached gigantic proportions giving an estimated 2,000 flashes of lightning. It had extended eastwards towards East Grinstead which was only just recovering from a deluge, 48 hours previously. The Furnace Pond burst its banks sweeping away an old mill and two cottages.

In the town, the rain was so heavy that manhole covers were forced up into the air by the pressure of water. It reminded one resident of ping-pong balls balancing on jets of water in a fairground shooting

West Sussex County Times front page, Friday, September 12th, 1958, with the headline "STORM COST — IT'S HUNDREDS OF THOUSANDS".

gallery. Many passengers were stranded at East Grinstead Station as a landslide blocked the line at Forest Row. The rain washed away two feet of topsoil at Tyes Cross, carving a 12-foot wide channel revealing underground drains. Weir Wood Reservoir, normally 40-feet deep, rose two feet and that represented an enormous volume of water that would otherwise have flowed into the River Medway.

In just 48 hours East Grinstead had recorded 4.7 inches (120mm) of rain. All this on top of a wet August which provided three unpleasant thunderstorms.At least one person speculated that it was all to do with atomic tests in the atmosphere!

The storm carved its way through Surrey and West Kent where, at Knockholt, it provided a two hour fall of rain, giving five inches (140mm) - Britain's second heaviest ever. In this area, new harrowing ordeals unfolded.

SUMMERS OF THE FIFTIES

THE decade of the 50's certainly had more than its fair share of poor summers with 1954, 1956 and 1958 being decidedly cool with lack of sunshine and wet conditions.

The day of the Queen's Coronation on 2nd June, 1953 was particularly cold with temperatures in the fifties and a blustery shower-laden north wind.

After the torrential rains of the 5th September, 1958 storm, many people complained that Sussex weather had been adversely affected by atomic bomb explosions. Perhaps the weather has a sense of humour, for there followed one of the most prolonged spells of fine weather Britain has ever experienced. The summer of 1959 was fine, warm and quite sunny, almost without interruption from May to October.

Tragedy at Gatwick

17th February, 1959

FOG was an unpleasant feature of the winter of 1958-9 and London particularly suffered many great "peasoupers". Aeroplanes, due to land at Heathrow, were diverted to the infant Gatwick Airport which certainly thrived on this unexpected business. The 26th January, 1959 was Gatwick's busiest day ever - "like Brighton beach on August Bank Holiday", said the *Crawley Observer*. It was due to the fog which clamped down on London, causing 25 aeroplanes to be diverted.

On 29th January, Gatwick was busier still and some 2,500 passengers were handled during the day, then an airport record. The Sussex airfield which was opened in June, 1958 soon welcomed its 250,000th passenger, confirming the need for an airport away from fog-bound London. Celebrations had barely died down when tragedy struck.

At 4.47 pm on the afternoon of Tuesday 17th February, 19 passengers and a crew of six, ploughed into a wood at Rusper, near Horsham in dense fog. Diverted to Gatwick because of fog in London, the Viscount ripped the tops off trees alongside the Rusper-Newdigate Road and tore through a copse before disintegrating. The tail broke off and from the gaping hole it left staggered the Turkish Prime Minister and two Government colleagues.

Rescuers from the Rusper area used penknives in an attempt to cut victims from the trangled wreckage. Fifteen people were killed but 10 survived. The Turkish leader, Mr Adrian Menderes, was looked after by Mrs Margaret Bailey and her husband of Oaklands Parks Farm, Rusper.

Across England, January, 1959 had only three fog-free days. In Crawley, Mrs N. Longley, whose records went back to 1921, registered the driest of all Februaries in 1959. Rainfall was a mere 0.09 inches (2.3mm).

Bathers at Eastbourne in the summer of 1959 which was one of the sunniest of the century. The peak of the heatwave occurred in early July when the temperature soared into the nineties. Even as late as 11th September a reading of 86F (30C) was recorded at Gatwick. In high summer Eastbourne averages seven hours' sunshine a day which makes it the sunniest seaside resort in Britain.

CHAPTER NINE

Shivering in the Sixties

In February, 1960, the Prime Minister, Mr Harold Macmillan, a Sussex resident, spoke about the wind of change that was blowing through the country. If he had been talking in a meteorological sense he would have been quite right. After the baking year of 1959, heavy rain fell in 1960. The most memorable weather event was the winter of 1962-63, the coldest overall since 1740, but 1968 will be remembered for many years for its infamous September floods.

1960: A wet year, especially in the autumn. On 3rd November, Tunbridge Wells recorded 2.2 inches (56mm) of rain and Brighton, 2.1 inches, while Eastbourne had its wettest November since records began there in 1886. Many places experienced 20 inches (500mm) of rain during the autumn, not far short of London's annual average.

1961: Spring came early with temperatures above 60F (16C) in February and 70F (21C) in March. In this month, many parts of Sussex had only one day of rain. On 2nd September, the temperature soared to 90F (32C) at Gatwick, but during Christmas it was very frosty and the year went out in a snowstorm.

1962: The year began and ended in deep snow and the summer was poor, remaining below 80F (26.5C). On the morning of 2nd June, an air frost "burnt" tender plants from Midhurst to Rustington.

1963: The coldest winter since 1740. At Fernhurst, the temperature plunged to 3F (-16C) on 23rd January. Inland, parts of Sussex were snow covered throughout the first two months. In a rather cool summer, Littlehampton held the distinction of enjoying the warmest day in Britain with 84F (29C).

1964: Cold weather brought Christmas card scenes to the Rowfant area on 12th-13th January, with every bough, branch and twig laced in a filigree of snow. After a dry winter, it turned wet with Worthing experiencing its wettest June since 1887.

1965: March began in an extremely wintry manner with six inches of snow and ended with summerlike heat and temperatures in the seventies. In the autumn, a rainfall of note was measured at Brighton with three inches (75 mm) on 20th November as a depression tracked across northern France.

1966: It looked as though winter was going to be long and severe as an area of high pressure over Scandinavia in January sent cold easterly winds across Britain. At Crawley, the temperature dropped to 14F (-10C). On the 20th, with a deep low moving towards the south-west approaches, a classic snowstorm seemed likely especially as temperatures were still several degrees below freezing. However, at breakfast time it rained. Mild air had spread in over a layer of cold, dense air near the ground and, like 1940, coated surfaces in a film of ice. In these treacherous conditions, 25 casualties were taken to Crawley Hospital, possibly their record number of "weather injuries" for a single day. A spokesman said they were falling down in Crawley like ninepins.

1967: In a wetter than average year, Eastbourne and Worthing managed an absolute drought for 27 days in June and July. The year was also notable for the early winter outburst of polar air which led to "snow Friday" along the Sussex coast on 8th December.

1968: On the morning of 1st July, many people awoke to a technicolour surprise. On hot southerly winds, a dust of fine sand and clay particles had fallen, mixed with rain drops. Red, orange and yellow spots covered newly cleaned cars. It was estimated that several thousand tons of the Sahara fell on England that day. Another substance that fell in quantity was rain. In a 70-year continuous record kept by Sir Norman and Lady Longley at Crawley from 1922, September 1968 proved to be the wettest month of all with 9.5 inches (243mm) and disastrous flooding.

1969: A remarkable spell of dry weather gave Brighton just 0.3 inches (8mm) of rain during the whole of September and October. The weather broke in November when a series of thunderstorms gave hail, torrential rain and squalls, gusting to 76 mph. During the middle of the month, trees fell, roofs were torn off and roads badly flooded.

Lewes - a town under siege

29th October - 4th November, 1960

IT had been one of the wettest Octobers ever known in Sussex. Day after day the rain poured down relentlessly from a leaden sky and by the 29th millions of gallons had collected on the Downs and the swollen rivers were threatening to burst their banks. East and West Sussex was on a flood alert. Those who lived in the river valleys watched and waited, hoping the crisis would pass.

On Sunday 30th October a few spots of rain fell again and on Monday it became a deluge. The river levels, supplemented by the water which cascaded down the hillsides, rose higher and higher until they were unable to cope with the sheer weight and speed of the water. Defences capitulated and vast lakes were created. Swirling brown floods rushed through towns, villages and hamlets, embracing everything in their reach. Vehicles floated away, so did furniture, clothing and debris. People were trapped in upstairs rooms. Trees and shrubs were torn from the ground as the rain, hissing and bubbling as it landed, flooded areas which had never been flooded before.

No town fared in Sussex worse than Lewes where the River Ouse overtopped the bridges, smashed defences and swept into the lower town. It slopped against doors and windows, burst them open and swept goods from the shelves. In Cliffe and Malling where the Ouse rose three feet above street level, dozens of families were evacuated and businesses put out of action.

Altogether, more than 620 homes were flooded and scores of offices, shops and factories badly damaged. In some directions Lewes was cut off by road and rail. Motorists entering the town from Uckfield and Brighton were sent back by the police. In the Waterbourne area the cattle market was flooded and the railway line resembled a fast flowing canal. Amphibious vehicles took people to places of safety. Elderly people were given temporary accommodation as the police, fire brigade, army, ambulance services, the WRVS, the Red Cross and a host of volunteers co-operated in a massive rescue and mopping up operation. A disaster fund was opened by the Mayor.

At Brighton, more than 500 telephones were out of action as the floods played havoc with underground cables. At Patcham, water poured off the Downs in torrents and Brighton's firemen and corporation staff launched their "battle of the basements", pumping 15 million gallons out of the Patcham flood area. The level of underground water resources rose an incredible 75 feet above normal.

At Hove, some 1,800 graves in the old Shoreham Road cemetery showed signs of sinking and 200 telephone lines were out of order. At Rustington, where the situation was changing hourly, roads were flooded for most of the week and water swirled into the telephone exchange with disastrous results. At Upper Portslade, a bucket blocked the storm water sewer and caused massive flooding. Children from a nearby school waded knee-deep in order to get home.

West Sussex did not escape. Bognor Regis, Felpham, Ferring and East Preston were the worst affected. Swirling flood waters halted traffic on the main roads and, at one time, it was impossible to get through to Chichester or Littlehampton . The village of Yapton was cut off for 22 hours.

At Worthing, calls for help were being received every few minutes at the police and fire stations. Roads were under two feet and water poured into the Plaza Cinema. At Angmering station, passengers on a stranded train had to make a detour across the field to the east in order to escape the floods.

As Sussex, and especially Lewes, counted the cost of the disaster, there was a motion in the House of Commons for a national fund. Thousands of communities in England and Wales had suffered and, in the West Country, some lives were lost. For the Sussex Fire Brigade the November floods of 1960 provided the largest pumping operation of all. There was, for them, a silver lining. The 5th November fell right in the middle of the emergency. Guy Fawkes night was a damp squib and no calls were received for bonfires out of control.

Lewes also had to call off the town's popular traditional bonfire night celebrations. Little wonder. For almost a week the town was under siege and it was almost two weeks before the Brighton Road, cut off at Falmer, was re-opened.

Lewes, where 620 homes were flooded.

The flooded streets of Lewes in the first week of November, 1960.

The flooded Rother Valley, upstream to Bodiam in November, 1960 after a week of torrential rain and 90 mph gales. The Rother Valley, to Rye, took on the appearance of a massive lake.

At first glance this looks like the Lewes Canal, but a second look will confirm that it is, in fact, the railway station in 1960, with flood water on the tracks almost up to platform level. In the background is the Castle and old town.

Coldest winter since 1740

The winter of 1962-3

A FEW flakes of snow fluttered gently to a frost-bound earth from a steel-grey sky. There was hardly a breath of wind. The afternoon of Boxing Day, 1962 was to be the last time that many parts of Sussex were to be free of a thick mantle of snow, until early March. The coldest winter since 1740 was about to begin.

The snow continued to fall throughout the 27th. It lay to a depth of 10 inches on the runway at Gatwick, necessitating the removal of 600 tons of snow in a massive clearance operation, while 50 outgoing flights were cancelled.

Worse was to follow as a deepening area of low pressure off the Brest Peninsular threw up a band of fine, powdery, drifting snow from the Channel coast. As winds reached gale force, many areas were brought to a standstill. At West Hoathly, four buses became stranded in drifts. An expectant mother gave birth in an ambulance as she was being taken to hospital; the vehicle had ploughed into a massive snowdrift between Balcombe and Cuckfield. Further south, deep drifts made it impossible for Upper Beeding district nurse, Kathleen Donnington to reach Edburton Sands. A helicopter from RAF Tangmere came to the rescue so she could give assistance to a diabetic patient who needed insulin.

Meanwhile, three people became trapped on Wigginholt Common between Pulborough and Coolham. They had been to a party and were driving home at 2.30 am when their car ran into a bank of snow. They tried to go for help but icy winds drove them back and they spent an uncomfortable night in the car with the engine turned on at intervals for warmth. They were rescued next day by a four-wheel drive truck and taken to Storrington.

It was the same all over Sussex. Snowploughs and a fleet of lorries cleared nine inches of snow from the centre of Chichester. On the London to Eastbourne Road from Wych Cross to Forest Row, high on the Ashdown Forest, 70 cars and lorries had to be dug out of drifts. The normally busy Imberhorne Lane, near East Grinstead remained impassable for three days. Some 95,000 miles of road throughout Britain were snow-bound. At Horsham, 19 inches of snow had fallen between the 26th and the end of December and gutters everywhere collapsed under its weight. In hundreds of communities delivery men were unable to call and large queues formed outside village shops.

The prolonged cold that followed the snow during

13th January, 1963 and "sea frazzle" is seen at Rottingdean.

A double decker is abandoned in King's Drive, Eastbourne in January, 1963.

January caused the sea to freeze for 100 feet off-shore at Eastbourne along a two-mile stretch of coast. The River Arun, Britain's second fastest flowing river, froze in places. There were reports from East Grinstead that foxes were hunting in pairs in the town centre and cat owners were advised to keep their pets indoors.

At Brighton, during this severe spell, for 27 days the temperature remained below freezing and at Hastings there was a snow-cover on 54 days. High pressure had settled to the north and north-east of Britain giving rise to persistent easterly winds from a frozen Europe. "When the wind is in the East, 'tis neither good for man nor beast".

The freezing weather co-incided with a "work to rule" by power workers. There was a break in supply. Thousands of homes in Brighton were without electricity for several hours and a baby in Shoreham was delivered by candlelight. As the weather showed no signs of relenting, a football pools panel was inaugurated for the first time.

February, too, was dominated by easterly winds. Parts of West Sussex had three inches of snow in just an hour on the 1st. The winter was estimated to have claimed the lives of 49 people, including one man who died while digging his car out of the snow at Langley Green on the northern edge of Crawley. There were lighter moments. A sense of together-ness and comradeship developed as people started to chat to strangers in the streets. And there was joy among ornithologists at Weir Wood where a snow goose was spotted on the reservoir - the first sighting in the area since 1937.

Slowly, very slowly, winter released its icy grip and the end of February brought deep blue skies and welcome sunshine. On Lywood Common, near Horsted Keynes, snowdrops nodded their heads in the breeze and as March appeared, Sussex was verdant again.

Bognor Regis in January, 1963 , where frozen snow was piled high on the beach. The sea was frozen along many stretches of shore, and in Chichester Harbour to a depth of seven inches.

Taken at Scotsford Lane, Broad Oak, Heathfield on 27th December, 1962 this photograph features Mr Bert Luck who was in charge of the local snow clearance operation. Mr Pain, the photographer recorded that the snow drift reached a height of 23 feet and six inches

Skating on the South Pond at Midhurst in 1963.

This snowdrift at Boreham Lane, Hailsham was 14 feet high. The road was blocked for two days. The photograph was taken after the late December falls in 1962.

Gigantic ice floes in Newhaven Harbour illustrate the severity of the winter of 1963.

GALES battered Sussex during the night of 20th January, 1965 and continued even more furiously the next morning. At the Domesday village of Felpham, thousands of gallons of muddy sea water poured into the village at a spot where Bognor Urban Council had planned to build a new 5,700 foot long seawall. Waves up to 20 feet high were reported by the coastguards at Selsey. Some of them burst over bungalows on the seafront.

Eastbourne, pictured above, took a terrible pounding. Waves broke over the promenade between the Albion Hotel and the Redoubt, tossed heavy metal seats about, ripped up paving slabs and tore down a lamp standard.

Hoad's Windmill in Gunter's Lane, Bexhill was a popular landmark for many years and used by the Royal Navy as a navigational aid. It was even painted by L.S. Lowry in 1960. The windmill was destroyed in the storm of 1965 and today only a post remains.

A convoy going nowhere

8th December, 1967

IT was like the end of the world to those who looked out of their windows in Rottingdean. The village was choked with a petrified forest of abandoned vehicles and Marine Drive was in a state of siege. Suddenly, the eyes of the nation were on this part of Sussex, gripped by a savage snowstorm.

Cold, northerly winds had spread south on 6th December, 1967. Embedded in the airstream was a "polar low", an area of snow which traversed England and hit the south coast around mid-day on the 8th. As it reached the warm waters of the Channel it became more potent to give a prolonged spell of heavy snow. Although the deepest falls were confined to a narrow coastal strip, this contained some of the most highly populated parts of Sussex.

The day started normally like many other cold December mornings. By the afternoon, Brighton was experiencing a raging blizzard with chaos and disruption to services. Many commuters spent the night in hotels rather than attempting the journey home.

In Rottingdean, 340 men, women and children were put up in the White House Hotel and a further 80 accommodated in guest houses, schools, the Red Cross Centre and cafes. The port's day club for the retired in Newhaven had an unexpected 70 guests for the night, including two boys who were picked up by the police, having attempted to walk home. Passengers on a ferry from Dieppe had to remain on board as all links to and from the port were severed.

Brighton Ambulance Service was forced to abandon 13 vehicles. One crew took five hours to answer a call on the edge of town while another was stranded at Rottingdean with eight patients who could not walk far. They spent the night in the Red Cross hall and the driver had to negotiate with local shops for food on credit since they had no money.

There was a veritable cascade of snow which reached a depth of 12 to 18 inches with massive drifts. Children were trapped in schools, the mayor of Brighton and his clerk were stranded in the town hall, 500 students were unable to leave the University. At Woodingdean, 100 employees were trapped in the Sunblest Bread factory but they continued to make bread. Local people, in long queues, bought loaves at the factory gates. It was a bumper time for the corner shops. One grocer in Hangleton said it was like Piccadilly Circus and business was brisk. A baker sold 900 loaves at Woodingdean and a long queue snaked down the road at Bobby's Bakery, Peacehaven.

When an event such as this occurs, routine is thrown into stark relief and sometimes becomes a matter of life or death. Two Hove ambulance drivers, Graham Cooper, a Sussex cricketer and Alan Earl had to journey to Haywards Heath to bring back a new-born baby in an incubator. Having spent nearly an hour trying to leave Brighton, they reached the hospital and picked up the baby and a nurse. It was then that the real drama began as the road was choked with traffic slipping and sliding to a halt. The temperature in the incubator kept dropping and so, in this moment of dire emergency, they crossed to the north-bound carriageway and proceeded south with bell ringing and lights flashing. At times Mr Earl had to disembark and walk in front. It took eight hours to reach Brighton. They arrived with the help of 40 people pushing them along New England Road. Mission completed, Graham Cooper had a two-hour walk home.

A boy nearly died when an air vent became blocked by snow as he was having a bath. Unconscious, he slipped under the water. His mother dragged him out and his brother-in-law administered the "kiss of life". He recovered. Five people were not so lucky, including one man who collapsed and died helping to free a car at the Devil's Dyke and another who was taken to a house in Coldean, suffering from hypothermia. He died sitting by the fire.

Elsewhere, Worthing had six foot drifts; a horse box with six horses inside was stuck in the snow all night with the police and RSPCA in attendance. Eastbourne was like a ghost town littered with abandoned vehicles and all roads into Lewes were blocked.

Luckily, after the coldest night since January, 1963 the weather relented. Mild air spread in from the Atlantic and the snows began to melt. The chaos of Snow Friday, as it became known, could not melt from the memories of those who lived in this corner of Sussex. One man, who had trudged down the hill towards Rottingdean, described the view: "It was an incredible sight; a convoy of buses, some with their lights on and engines running and nearly all crowded with passengers, but going nowhere. There were half a dozen lorries and one articulated giant jacknifed across the Rottingdean crossroads and, between them, scores of cars waiting for help."

Rottingdean on 8th December, 1967 - a convoy of cars, buses and lorries going nowhere.

The wild, wild waters

14th - 16th September, 1968

LIGHTNING flashed, thunder rolled and the rain fell in torrents. Not particularly unusual, except that it did not stop. Hour after hour, rain of tropical proportions cascaded down, resulting in the worst floods ever to be witnessed in north west Sussex. Every low-lying town was inundated by waves of muddy water.

Saturday 14th September, 1968 had already brought some hefty thunderstorms and now, on the following morning, an almost Stygian gloom descended on the land as the rain poured down. The culprit was a rapidly deepening depression to the south west of Britain which extended a trough of low pressure across the south east along which there were some large vertical motions of the atmosphere. It became stationary over Sussex and that meant prolonged, heavy rain.

By Sunday morning some 525 tons of water had fallen per acre in the Crawley area on already saturated ground. Rivers were quick to burst their banks. At Newbridge, it was a night of high drama. Three cars in a convoy tried to cross the bridge, but by now the swirling waters of the River Arun were racing along at 15 knots, sweeping over the structure and forcing the travellers onto the roofs of their vehicles.

A lady and her 15-year-old daughter were engulfed and carried away. Their screams for help were mingled with the thunderous roar of the river. For one and a half miles, the girl was hurtled along in the coal-black night by the angry waters, until her harrowing journey was halted by a clump of bramble bushes that had been thrust in the waters from an uprooted tree. By the light of a torch a farm worked found the girl, shocked and exhausted. He took her to Guildenhurst Manor and later she recovered in Worthing Hospital. The mother died but her 11-year-old son, who was also in the car, and some other motorists were rescued by a team that included coastguards from Shoreham.

Helicopters came to the aid of an elderly couple at Pulborough where their house was entirely surrounded by floodwater, and at Bucks Green, near Rudgwick, a 25-year-old man climbed a tree as the water rose alarmingly. He was seen, waving frantically, by an air-sea rescue team from Thorney Island.

At one time Billingshurst was cut off completely when the main road crumbled, and then subsided, under the impact of swirling torrents of flood water. A Pulborough family had to be rescued by a police-man in a boat. The waters were reaching half way up the walls of their bungalow in Swan Corner and the heroic sergeant got out of his boat and waded up to his neck to affect the rescue. One policeman, Leonard Oborne, was later awarded an OBE for his part in the rescue operation around Pulborough.

West Sussex Fire Brigade answered 396 calls for assistance in under 24 hours. They evacuated people from the upper storeys of their houses at Ebernoe and Wisborough Green, and at a retirement home at Stopham where 36 people had to leave a building, encircled by floods. In Horsham, the normally placid stream, Red River received an unwelcome boost when sluice gates were opened at Warnham Mill Pond to prevent their total collapse. The turbulent stream then entered the Arun, to swell it even further. At Blackridge Lane, it was 10 feet above normal height. One man who had just bought his bungalow, watched in horror as floodwater pushed through the front door and out of the back. Furniture was soon afloat.

In Fordingbridge Close, houses were almost submerged with furniture touching the ceiling. In gardens, all that was visible were the tops of sheds and greenhouses. Anxious relatives found it impossible to contact victims as telephone were inoperative.

By Monday, many roads were still under water and commuters took some circuitous routes to the office. People travelling from Hastings to London were diverted via Eastbourne, Haywards Heath and Croydon. Rail and road bridges took a tremendous pounding, particularly the Chaffield Bridge, north of Pensfold and the Burcham Bridge on the Horsham to Brighton road.

Air travellers had problems. Gatwick was surrounded by floodwater and telephones were out of order. The car parks had become lakes and abandoned cars littered the approach roads. A helicopter managed to take off from Redhill with vital blood plasma for hospitals along the south coast.

The damage caused by the September rains of 1968 in the South East assumed disaster proportions. An estimated 1,000 square miles were under water. Some places recorded as much as a third of their annual rainfall in just two days. In the 70 years of records kept by Sir Norman and Lady Longley at their Meteorological Office-monitored rainfall station in Crawley, Sunday 15th September, 1968 was their wettest day ever with 3.65 inches (93mm). The month was the wettest ever with 9.50 inches (243mm).

September 15th, 1968 and a tale of two fire engines. Above, the tender drives through the flooded streets of Horsham to help pump out thousands of gallons of water. Below, the traffic lights by Stopham Bridge over the Arun are red, but so what ? This vehicle, owned by the Fire Brigade, is going nowhere until the water recedes.

This is the town centre of Uckfield on 22nd November, 1974 after the River Uck had burst its banks, flooded the railway station and two feet of swirling brown water had burst into the High Street. The culprit was torrential rain which caused roads, railways and airports to be closed and inundated hundreds of acres of farmland.

At Lewes, anxious eyes were being kept on the Winterbourne stream. At Southbourne, near Chichester, the A 27 was closed. At Hassocks, two feet of dirty water flowed into shops when storm drains packed up. At Ifield, nurses were carried over swirling torrents by gallant workmen. At Steyning, householders in night clothes, struggled to get furniture, carpets and other possessions out of harm's way. At Horsham, a lady found four feet of water in her kitchen at St Mary's Walk and at Three Bridges, the industrial estate at Stephenson's Way was completely cut off.

Nowhere, however, was as bad as Uckfield where the water collected goods from the Keymarket supermarket and washed them into the High Street. Children waded into the water to salvage the damaged stock. Brighton, too, had a disastrous time, especially at Bodiam Close, suitably nicknamed "Mud Row" because of persistent flooding.

CHAPTER TEN

A window on the seventies

After the blizzards and floods of the sixties, there was no remission from snow and rain during the next decade. Hastings, particularly, suffered on several occasions, although not on the disastrous scale of 1960, 1963 or 1968. The seventies, however, will be remembered for the sensational, never-to-be forgotten year of 1976, when the county basked in record hours of sunshine, drought restrictions were introduced and people were told to share a bath with a friend.

1971: The temperature on 6th March at Fairlight was only 28F (-2C) and 16F (-9C) at East Hoathly, with a cover of snow. Along the Sussex coast the June rainfall amounted to almost five times the average. On 19th December, in violent squalls, Newhaven recorded a wind speed of 104 mph.

1972: A brief spell of cold easterlies sent the temperature down to 5F (-15C) at Fernhurst on the 31st January. The Royal Sovereign Lighthouse off Eastbourne reported a steady wind of 64 mph (a violent storm of the Beaufort scale) during 13th November. On 3rd December, three inches of hail fell in 15 minutes in Bognor.

1973: The driest year in the Crawley record with just 22.69 inches (576mm) of rain.

1974: Incredibly this was the record year in the Crawley record. Rain amounted to 46.55 inches (1182mm) - more than double the year before. A Mr Grossmark of Brighton was on passage by boat from Gosport to Newhaven on the 18th August when he was almost encircled by six water spouts which made a solid foundtain of spray 300 feet high.

1975: A warm, sunny summer was preceded by snow falling at Hassocks on 2nd June.

1976: The long period of excessive heat and drought caused serious outbreaks of woodland and grass fires. West Sussex Fire Brigade tackled 1,579 countryside and garden fires throughout the year, which resulted in a massive overtime bill Tempers frayed as some people defied a hosepipe ban. One man, suspected of clandestine watering activities in his garden, found his hose cut into little pieces at Hassocks.

1978: Furious gales on 11th January causing structural damage. There were blizzards on 31st December.

Mrs Joan Hutley, of Munnion Road, Ardingly, had a heatwave surprise in 1976 when her Yucca plant bloomed for the first time. Despite being a native of Mexico and Central America, it still wilted in the high temperatures of June 1976.

1979: The winter of discontent. Snow fell on strikers huddled around bonfires at picket lines. On 29th January, black ice caused more than 30 accidents on the A23 between London and Brighton. At Warninglid Five Ways, a driver was trapped in the wreckage of his car and the fire engine going to the rescue also skidded on the ice and overturned, trapping a fireman. On 26th January, 100 passengers waited for two hours at Hassocks while iced rail lines were cleared. British Rail claimed that the conditions were the "worst since 1947".

Dreaming of a white Christmas

December, 1970

CHRISTMAS comes but once a year. White ones less often; in fact it is a rare occurrence in Sussex.

In 1970, snow fell over the region on Christmas Day for the first time since 1956 and the *Crawley Advertiser* commented: "Yes, it was the White Christmas we had all been dreaming about, but with these greeting card scenes come chaos".

Gatwick Airport had dozens of flights cancelled or delayed and at one stage so many passengers were stranded that some had to be accommodated at hotels in Brighton. On Boxing Day, the runways were closed for seven hours because of deep snow.

In Crawley New Town, 4.5 inches of snow lay and parks became winter playgrounds for hundreds of youngsters enjoying tobogganing or snowball fighting. There was great confusion on the railways with hour-long delays on the Gatwick-Horsham service.

WHITE CHRISTMASES IN SUSSEX

The criteria for a White Christmas is that snow must fall on Christmas Day. The following includes snow falling - and settling.

1906: Several inches.

1927: Classic snowstorm.

1938: Snow fell every day from 18th December.

1956: An inch or two on Christmas night.

1970: Between four to eight inches. A classic White Christmas.

Some slight falls occurred in 1917 and 1968. In 1981 the ground was snow covered across much of Sussex but no snow actually fell.

The Sealink Ferry between Newhaven and Dieppe has sailed in some rough seas, but few can remember conditions as bad as they were on 7th September, 1974. The photograph shows the ferry as she battled with the waves, surmounting each crest and then falling dramatically as she hit the succeeding troughs. It was exhilarating to watch but a quite different sensation was felt by the passengers!

So who's dreaming of a white Easter? ran the headlines. It certainly looked that way on Thursday 27th March, 1975 when the biggest snowfall for some years turned parts of Sussex into a Christmas card scene. On the East Dean Road across Beachy Head, Race Hill (pictured above) and other exposed areas, the snow was more than three inches deep. New born lambs had an early taste of a Sussex winter.

Thousands of trees toppled in a severe gale on 2nd January, 1976. The worst damage was in the Midlands, but the wind was strong enough to cause much structural damage across Sussex. Here workmen clear away a tree which crashed in Haywards Heath.

Top of the sunshine league

Blazing Year of 1976

ON the 31st August, 1976 a few drops of rain fell and holidaymakers on the south coast cheered. It made headline news, for this was the first hint that the great heatwave had ended. It was a heatwave which delighted Britons, worried the Government, threatened industry and left millions under drought restrictions.

There had not been a summer like it this century. Temperatures soared and all parts of Sussex basked in record hours of sunshine. With much of the county receiving less than 60 per cent of its average rainfall between May 1975, and August, 1976, this represented the worst drought since 1727 when rainfall records of any accuracy were first kept.

If holidaymakers loved it, so did the media. We were told by one national newspaper to put a brick in our toilet cisterns, or even to share a bath with a friend. For 16 consecutive days the temperature somewhere in England reached, or exceeded, 90F (32C), an unprecedented event. Suddenly it was a time for barbecues, bikinis, endless queues for ice creams and, in the Sussex seasides towns, numerous bad cases of sunburn.

Sussex became tinder dry. Fires broke out right across the county with thousands of calls for assistance. Hard-pressed fire crews were often in action a long way from base as fires raged on the Downs and in the forests. In some areas of the Ashdown Forest, firemen watched, almost impotently, as hundreds of acres were destroyed.

In June, Eastbourne enjoyed 323 hours of sunshine - enough to put it on top of the sunshine league above Shanklin, Margate, Hastings and Littlehampton - the other top four. The sea temperatures were the highest ever recorded at an average of 66F. As temperatures steamed into the 90's at the end of June an extraordinary situation developed at Horsham swimming baths. Inside, 600 people, cooling themselves in the water, refused to leave. Long queues formed outside, demanding to be let in. Tempers began to fray and the police were called to persuade those on the inside to leave. There was no respite in July. Ambulancemen were daily collecting people overcome by the heat and firemen were sweltering it out against acres and acres of gorse and grass fires.

As August arrived with no sign of a break in the weather, the Government was becoming increasingly worried by a potentially disastrous national water shortage. In Sussex, the Ardingly Reservoir

---

BLAZING DAYS OF JUNE, 1976

26th June at North Heath 95.7F (35.4C)

26th June at Tun Wells 93.6F (34.2C)

27th June at Brighton 95F (35C)

28th June at Gatwick 91.4F (33C)

During the first eight days of July, the daily maximum temperature in Brighton never fell below 88F (31.1C). The town recorded a 36 day absolute drought in July - August with just 0.05 (1.3mm) of rain.

---

was dangerously low. Weir Wood, near East Grinstead and Bewl Water, just over the border in Kent were drying up and their clay bottoms were cracking in the heat.

Southern Water Company banned the use of hoses and sprinklers for the first time since 1947. Sussex householders were advised to water their gardens with bath water and Draconian penalties were introduced for anyone found defying the ban. A satellite picture taken on 21st August showed Britain devoid of cloud as the mercury rose yet again to the high eighties.

Ironically, as parts of Britain were experiencing a Mediterranean-like summer, reports came in from Hong Kong that it had been ravaged by Typhoon Ellen. A colossal 16 (420 mm) of rain fell in 24 hours, almost two-thirds of Sussex's yearly quota in one day.

In a state of desperation one water authority wrote to the Department of Cloud Physics in New South Wales asking for information on rainmaking. In London a guru prayed for rain, while the Government finally played its trump card and appointed a Minister of Drought. Almost as if it had a sense of humour, the weather gave way. The persistent block of high pressure broke down and it rained. A vicar asked his congregation to give thanks to the Almighty for the downpour.

The development of an upper trough to the southwest of Britain led to September being the second wettest over England since the early 18th century. The crisis was simply washed away.

*27th June, 1976. On one of the hottest days of the century, with temperatures in Sussex
outstripping those on the Continent, sunbathers on the beach at Brighton began casting off
bikini tops. No-one complained. "If they did, we would have to put a stop to it", said the police
at the time. At 2 pm the temperature recorded by Gatwick was 90F (32C). A peak of 95F was
reached in the mid-afternoon.*

Camel racing was one of the main attractions at the Haywards Heath Carnival on Saturday 10th July, 1976. On this day, at the height of the summer drought, there were 14 hours of sunshine in the South East. Four days earlier the temperatures had climbed to above 90F (32C). The camels felt quite at home.

A dried-up pond on a shimmering hot day in 1976 in the normally picturesque West Sussex village of Singleton.

The mill pond at West Ashling, near Chichester dried up in the summer of 1976 and great cracks appeared at the bottom.

CHAPTER ELEVEN

A glance at the eighties

Tornadoes, floods, blizzards, great deluges, gales at sea, hailstorms and even a crabstorm - the variety of the weather was considerable even before the onset of 1987. Then came the year of the century. It began with a blizzard and continued, in early October, with terrible floods It concluded with Sussex reeling from a "hurricane" that changed the face of the landscape, providing the greatest meteorological talking point of all. (See pages 134 - 153).

1980: On the 11th October, Sussex experienced its heaviest rainfall in one day when 5.2 inches (133mm) fell at Durrington, Worthing.

1981-2: Bitter cold and snowy spells during winter. A rare type of thunderstorm moved north from Brighton on 17th September, 1982. There was vivid lightning and deafening thunder, but no rain. October, however, provided relentless rain, with 8.65 inches (221mm) at Brighton.

1983: Hailstones, the size of golf balls fell on 5th June and yachts at sea capsized as they were hit by sudden squalls. At Brighton, dark heavy clouds rolled around the sky and a man repairing his car about a mile from the sea had the shock of his life when a crab dropped from the sky landing six feet from him. The creature was about 10 inches across. Mr Julian Gowan had hardly recovered when hailstones sent him diving for cover. Eye witnesses saw a water spout out to sea and it is possible that it jettisoned the unfortunate crab inland.

1983: July, 1983 was the warmest month ever recorded in Sussex with an average temperature of 68F (20C), or more.

On 6th August, 1981, a cloud 42,000 feet high turned day into night at Gatwick. The photograph of the British Caledonian building was taken at 11.30 am.

1984: Nearly an inch of rain from ex-hurricane, Hortense, fell at Horsham on 5th October..

1985: Severe cold affected Sussex during January and February with a total of 27 days snow cover. Farmers were able to cross the River Ouse by tractor. Snow lay eight inches deep in Crowborough on 16th January.

1986: The second coldest February of the century. The harbour at Rye froze and at Brighton there were nine ice days. Nowhere in the county did the tem-perature rise above 40F (4C). In a dismal August, East Hoathly boasted the nation's warmest day of the month with 79F (26C) on the 10th.

1988: The wettest January since 1877 at Hove was followed by 142 hours of February sunshine, an extraordinary 4.9 hours a day. There were only two sunless days.

1989: A very mild winter. On 25th February, Gatwick recorded the lowest air-pressure in Sussex this century of 951.6 millibars. Tunbridge Wells was rainless in May, and at Hove it was the warmest and driest since records were first kept.

1990: During the great gale on 25th January, Herstmonceux measured a gust speed of 99 mph. January and February together were the mildest for more than 300 years and the summer was again warm and sunny with a notable early August hot spell.

1990: A 110-foot high Wellingtonia tree at Isfield, near Uckfield was hit by a bolt of lightning and then shattered into splinters during a storm on 2nd November. The exploding evergreen badly damaged the roof of the lodge at Isfield Place but it was good news for Uckfield Young Farmers who collected the timber for their bonfire celebrations.

The Brighton junior ice hockey team play at Ditchling village pond in January, 1985.

More than an April shower

14th April, 1981

A DELUGE of rain, damaging lightning and great peals of thunder rumbling through the night are elements of our weather more commonly experienced in the warmer summer months. April is one of the driest months of the year and often associated with brief passing showers.

During the night and morning of 14th April, 1981 Horsham and district was swamped by a severe thunderstorm which gave as much as 3.6 inches (91 mm) of rain. Even Hove, well to the south of the main activity, had its wettest day of the century with 1.48 inches (39 mm).

In Horsham, the fire brigade received more than 100 calls for help, the first at 2.15 am. The village of Southwater was badly affected. Water lay two feet deep in the Hen and Chicken public house. Firemen knocked a hole in the kitchen floor to increase the depth in order to pump efficiently and they removed 10,000 gallons of water. A resident awoken by a loud crack of thunder found a downstairs carpet floating around the room. Some 15 appliances helped dry out the village and a self-help group of around 50 residents formed a human chain with buckets in Station Road in an attempt to drain water away from the houses.

Throughout the area the scale of flooding gave bus drivers a difficult time. Southdown manfully struggled on but in Billingshurst, Henfield, Partridge Green and Slinfold, floodwaters were just too deep.

In Horsham, a woman and her two children were asleep when a mighty bang was followed by the roof caving in. Plaster, ceiling joists, roofing felt, tiles and wiring collapsed into the room. The woman brushed away some rubble and went to her children. The eldest daughter had scrambled from the wreckage of her room after pulling plaster away from the youngest. They were unharmed.

The cause of the storm was the movement of warm air northwards over France which was forced to rise and precipitate by cooler denser air moving south over Southern England. The battle lines were drawn on a line from Brighton to Horsham.

The storm remained stationary and lightning strikes and flooding led to 4,000 consumers losing their power supplies. Commuters were frustrated by flooding at the Worthing Road railway bridge on the southern edge of Horsham and trains from Bognor were turned back.

Two weeks later, many parts of England were brought to a standstill by severe snow-storms. Sussex, on this occasion, was spared.

An aerial view of Horsham, showing the flooded streets, after one of the most severe thunderstorms of the century on 14th April, 1981.

Rivers reach crisis levels

2nd February, 1983

ON the day the massive gates of London's new £435 million flood barrier were raised for the first time, five coastal towns in Sussex went on to an emergency flood alert as rivers reached crisis levels. In Newhaven, Camber, Rye, Shoreham and Littlehampton, families waited with great anxiety as water lapped at their front doors. Their fears were well founded. In the early hours of 2nd February, 1983, a "freak" tide brought the sea swirling into town centres, causing the worst flooding that many could remember.

At Newhaven, families were treated for shock after being evacuated from their homes in Chapel Street, which backs on to the harbour quay. All ten homes in the street were flooded with three feet of water, electricity was cut and, as firemen spent all day pumping out hundreds of gallons, inhabitants did their best to rescue furniture and fittings awash in muddy river water.

In Shoreham, police and firemen woke people living next to the Adur to warn them that the river was spilling its bank. In Littlehampton, muddy water affected dozens of homes and residents said the damage was "the worst in living memory". At Elmer Sands, near Bognor, social services were called in to help evacuate a 98-year-old woman, whose home was threatened. At Camber, houses stood like islands in a sea of water.

Neighbours rally to help. A sodden carpet is taken from a flooded house near the harbour in Newhaven.

A dog makes his way across a flooded road in Newhaven. This is 2nd February, 1983.

The only way to Woodingdean on 2nd March, 1986 was on foot after a heavy fall of snow had turned many Sussex roads, particularly those on the Downs, into scenes more in keeping with the icy wastes of Antarctica. The snow had arrived a few days earlier after the second coldest February of the century (after 1947). It snowed again on 1st March and for a few days the temperature remained below freezing all day while icy winds blew the snow into huge drifts. No wonder the road between Falmer and Rottingdean was impassable.

*Vivid and majestic flashes of lightning lit up the Hastings sky on 8th July, 1986 and caused
great consternation among brontophobics throughout the borough. Two houses were struck.
At 13 Collinswood Drive, St. Leonards, lightning struck the chimney and travelled down the
cable television wire into the living room. At Yew Tree Close, The Ridge, bricks from the
chimney stack were thrown into the road. No-one was hurt.*

A landslide on the A 283 Washington to Steyning Road occurred in torrential rain on 19th November, 1986 when torrents of water cut a groove along the side of the road, which then collapsed. It was sealed off by the police.

Several homes on the seafront took the full brunt of this storm which reached its peak at high tide. One woman in Dane Close, Seaford was awoken by police in the early hours and when she opened the door, found herself actually standing in the sea. Waves were crashing right over the top of the house.

The most tragic incident took place on the A24 near Horsham when a cyclist, Cynthia Littlejohn aged 37, was hit by a car in heavy rain. The vehicle did not stop. The cyclist, lying injured on the road, was then struck by four other cars, whose drivers did not see her in the atrocious conditions. She was found dead by police.

In Wilmington Way, Haywards Heath, flat roofs from three adjoining houses were blown off by the gale-force winds.

A cyclist, well protected from the elements, pushes his bicycle along the icy road at Littlehampton in February, 1986 - one of the coldest months of the century.

The Selsey tornado

21st November, 1986

TORNADOES produce the most powerful winds on the earth's surface. They are violent vortices, spinning masses of air, where winds can attain values in excess of 200 mph. Their origin is complex but as a warm air mass is pushed out of the way by colder air tornadoes can form along the boundary. At sea they take the form of waterspouts.

It was such a situation on the night of 21st November, 1986. A vigorous cold front was crossing Selsey about an hour and a half after midnight causing heavy rain and thunder. What appeared to be a wall of water hit the Double Barn night club and, amid a cacophony of noise, two benches were flung into nearby trees. A waterspout had made landfall and, thereafter, on its journey across Selsey Bill it damaged 150 houses forcing the evacuation of 290 people. The swathe of destruction was no more than 200 feet wide, following an east-north-east track.

In Rusking Close, almost every house on the south side of the road suffered roof damage. One person described the noise as "like a steam train" while another said it was similar to a "jet coming into land".

Tornadoes often twist and distort trees. On the southern end of the headland, two trees had their tops severed at Seal Court and three more had similar treatment at Ursula Avenue. Not far away at Woodlands, in the direction of the storm track, a 40

foot high tree was completely uprooted. A deluge of rain accompanied the tornado and at Sunnymead Drive a blue fireball was seen, followed by an explosion.

All along the tornado's path there was a trail of wind-blown slates, smashed sheds and collapsed garages. Residents were so shocked that many were glad to be evacuated to village and church hall lest another whirlwind should rend the night. Meanwhile, emergency services made their broken properties safe. As a parting shot the vortex overturned an 18-foot boat before disappearing seawards from the shore adjacent to Beach Road.

Astonishingly there were no major injuries. An hour later, a tornado damaged some 50 houses at Lewes with the unlucky resident of one house arriving home to find that "most of the front windows were shattered, the front part of the roof was off, water was flooding in and two sheds and a greenhouse were blown down". One lady went to "put out a crate of empty milk bottles only to find, when she opened the door, the bottles shooting upstairs and out of the back windows". A Landport estate car was lifted up and tossed upside down.

There were similar stories at Portslade where houses lost tiles and two trees were uprooted. One house had its chimney stack toppled, accompanied by an unnerving sound like the roar of a jet.

Walking on Hedges

January, 1987

ON Saturday 10th January, 1987, snowflakes began to fall on Sussex. A little more than 24 hours later the whole of the county lay still and white in a trance of snow. By Wednesday there were no buses, no trains, no milk, no post, no schools and in many places, no telephones as the county slithered to a standstill in the most chaotic conditions since 1963.

The bitter weather came from Russia and Scandinavia. It was brought by icy winds, accompanied by snow showers in the day and penetrating frost at night. On Monday 12th January, the temperature had dropped to a bone-chilling 9F (-13C) at breakfast time and motorists, who ignored police warnings to stay at home unless their journey was really necessary, could only see the road ahead by constantly scraping frost off the inside of their windscreen. Daytime temperatures reached only 18F (-8C).

By Monday evening, the countryside lay under many inches of fresh, crisp, deep snow of inconceivable perfection and beauty after the coldest day since 1867. On Tuesday, ferocious easterly winds blew the snow into huge drifts, blocking many roads, railways and town centres. As the people of Sussex donned their moon boots and dragged the sledge, or even skied to the nearest shop, they were confronted by appalling visibility as clouds of icy crystals were blasted off fields by the gusting winds. It was possible to walk on hedges between Rottingdean and Woodingdean.

At Hastings, the minimum temperature was 14F (-9.8C), the lowest since 1947 and the only train to make it out of the station was the 5.30 am on Monday. It was later reported to be snowbound somewhere near Crowhurst. At Crawley, a baby was airlifted for special treatment in London after being born six weeks prematurely. An RAF helicopter with doctors and nurses on board arrived safely at Tooting Hospital's landing pad with little Nichole Deadman. At Henfield, the town's only supermarket closed on Tuesday due to a staff walkout over lack of heating. At Horsham, soldiers from the 6th and 7th Queen's Regiment delivered meals in Landrovers to elderly people cut off by snow.

In rural areas, the RAF and Army were involved in operations to help villagers cut off by snow drifts. Sheep farmers on the South Downs had an anxious time as the snow piled up and a round-the-clock vigil was organised. Horsham fireman, Rob Hyden, whose wife kept sheep on her 28-acre farm, had the perfect answer to tackle the Arctic wastes. A sleigh, carrying bales of hay, was pulled round the fields by his team of Siberian huskies. In the village of Itchingfield, farmer Tim Warren battled non-stop for two days with his bulldozer to prevent snow cutting off his village. His efforts were recognised by West Sussex County Council who agreed to pay for the cost of fuel !

Many local hospitals ran short of blood and emergency donor sessions were arranged. At Hastings, only routine admissions that didn't require blood were being accepted.

In the Chichester area, weather recording equipment at Goodwood airfield showed a lowest temperature of 9F (-13C) on the Monday night.

Hundreds of schools were closed and an added misery came from a number of burst pipes. In the battle against the big freeze, West Sussex Council sent 300 men into action in a 900 mile road salting operation that cost more than £900,000.

By the foggy morning of 19th January, a thaw had set in, and the giant icicles that hung from houses and shops had to be carefully removed by firemen as they presented a real risk of injury. Sussex slowly unfroze and life, for those who escaped the trauma of burst pipes and its accompanying chaos, returned to normal.

TEN OF THE SNOWIEST YEARS IN SUSSEX

DATE	DEPTH OF SNOW	TOWN	DATE	DEPTH OF SNOW	TOWN
			This table shows the level of snow - not drifting		
26th November, 1890	12inches	Crowborough	Late January, 1947	12inches	Crowborough
29th December, 1908	8inches	Horsham	26-29th Dec, 1963	19inches	Horsham
3rd-4th March, 1909	16inches	Tun Wells	8th Dec, 1967	18inches	Brighton
27th December, 1927	18inches	Crawley	12-14th Jan, 1987	16inches	Hastings
27th January, 1940	10inches	Eastbourne	7th-9th Feb, 1991	9inches	Tun Wells

The snow was four inches deep and a new blizzard made driving conditions perilous. This was Battle High Street in the early stages of the January 1987 freeze-up.

Not Siberia, but East Dean hill on 15th January, 1987. In these conditions two people were stranded in their car all night.

Mrs Carol D'Albertanson and her sons, Russell, 8 , and Oliver, 5, found their East Grinstead home festooned with icicles on Saturday 17th January, 1987.

Saltdean, near Brighton on 12th January, 1987 - the coldest day of the century. Occasionally this traffic snake moved, but only slowly.

The flooded Ouse Valley, near Lewes in October, 1987.

Floods across the county

October, 1987

OCTOBER, 1987 was the wettest month of this turbulent year. All along the river valleys of Sussex, police and firemen were polishing up on their emergency plan procedures after unprecedented torrents of rain. The Ouse had burst its banks near Lewes, the land around Alfriston was flooded by the swollen Cuckmere, the streets of Henfield, Warninglid, Pulborough and Slinfold were awash and the Rother, as usual, was dangerously high.

Eastbourne, too, had more than its share of rain. On 10th October, nearly two inches fell, making it the borough's highest rainfall in one day for 30 years. At Hailsham, a 51-year-old Crowborough man drowned when his car skidded off the A267, just north of the Boship roundabout, and plunged into a flooded field. He was discovered at the wheel of his partly submerged car by an AA patrolman, who himself had been blown off the road by torrential rain and high speed winds.

The stormy weather blew right along the south coast. Pebbles were strewn across promenades and hoteliers and guest house owners put out their sandbags as the sea threatened to invade. The land around Brighton was inundated and there was a great mudslide at Rottingdean.

What a dirty, wet, cold, windy year this was turning out to be. Perhaps the run-up to Christmas would be calmer !

The beautiful Cuckmere valley, near Alfriston, a favourite tourist spot, under water in October, 1987.

The Rottingdean mudslide

7th October, 1987

IN an incident more in keeping with a vulnerable riverside community in Bangladesh, a merciless torrent of mud and slime slithered down from the hills, swept across a road and carved an ugly trail of destruction before engulfing the heart of a pictur-esque village, several feet deep.

This wasn't Bangladesh. It was Rottingdean in Sussex on the night of 7th October, 1987 when more than 100 families found themselves surrounded, not only by mud, but earth, stubble, stones and slime. The damage was estimated at more than £1 million.

The mudslide came from farm fields on the hill-side above Rottingdean, where hedges had been removed and the furrows for seeds drilled in lines up the hill instead of across it. After days of heavy rain, thousands of gallons of water had collected in the fields to the east of the Falmer Road. Suddenly, the saturated earth could take no more and the sheer weight of the flood water swept 28 acres of soil on its trail of destruction. It poured through the farm and was so powerful that it took the door off a barn that stood in its way. It was an unbelievable sight resembling molten lava flowing towards the village.

Police officer Andy Sewell watched in horror as the mud enveloped a car that was passing the field. The car was caught right in the middle of the landslide and when it finally came to a halt it was stuck in three or four feet of mud. The policeman helped the elderly couple to escape. The mudslide then passed along Court Ord Road, Eley Drive, Meadow Close and into Rottingdean High Street. Residents looked from their windows to see cars and vans floating into driveways. Two cars smashed into houses, brick walls buckled under the pressure, wooden fences were washed away. When it finally came to a halt, it reached half way up a bright red postbox. This remained the high point for hours to come.

Many people in Rottingdean were settling down to an evening in front of the TV, thankful to be insu-lated from the high winds and heavy rain that was lashing most of Sussex. Floods had been forecast - from the sea, not from the hills. Mrs Jean Beves was watching the storm from her bedroom window in Falmer Road when she saw what looked like a huge black wave. She wasn't too sure what was happen-ing until the mud crashed through her fence and hit the house. Within minutes the 'fridge was floating out of the kitchen and the whole of the ground floor of the house was ruined.

Police and firemen toured the area and advised people to switch off all power except an electric light. They brought in extra sandbags as a threatening lagoon of water remained in the field. Helped by council workmen, hundreds of people battled throughout the night to keep the drains clear and the next day began the massive task of shovelling away the grime.

Sheep are rescued from Cold Blow Farm, Laughton, near the scene of the mudslide.

The path of the mudslide down Falmer Road, Rottingdean on 7th October, 1987.

In the wake of the "hurricane"

16th October, 1987

BLIZZARDS, gales, floods and mudslides. What more could Mother Nature hurl at Sussex in this extraordinary year of 1987 ? The answer came in the dark, early hours of Friday 16th October. As an unsuspecting county slept, a storm was brewing in the English Channel. It was destined to be the most devastating meteorological event of the century.

The storm, driven on by hurricane-force winds came ashore at Sussex in the small hours. At first , milk bottles rolled and dustbin lids cartwheeled down the road. The wind increased in speed and violence, grabbing all in its path, shaking, twisting, tossing and roaring. Hotel roofs were torn asunder, caravan parks reduced to matchwood, cars crushed by falling trees and communications crippled. As the storm travelled inland it unravelled what had been knitted by time. Ancient trees, in the forests and on the Downs, were toppled and tall pines beheaded. It changed the face of the landscape and went on to dislocate Kent, Surrey, London and the eastern counties.

There had been nothing unusual about the weather forecast. Storm winds were reported to be sweeping across the Atlantic but they were going to miss Britain. At 2 am, trees started to go down in the Isle of Wight. It was not later than 2.30 when Ronald Davies was killed by a chimney falling through four floors of the Queen's Hotel at Hastings. At the same time the high-voltage power lines from Dungeness were "tripping" as flying debris caused short circuits. Throughout Sussex, trees fell onto power cables. Soon the county was in darkness.

The power of the wind, reaching speeds in excess of 100 miles an hour, was now destroying the work of many centuries. Sussex was wide awake. People moved their families into "safe" rooms or cellars. Others pulled on their boots and foolishly walked into the teeth of the storm. Stories were beginning to unfold, more than any chronicler could begin to assemble, stories that were hair-raising, grotesque, heroic and tragic. Life in this bewildered county came to a standstill and for a while developed a new pace of candlelit meals without television or telephone. Statistics abounded as the final cost was evaluated in billions. The "Hurricane" of 1987 passed into folklore.

"Why were we not warned?", the people of Sussex demanded. Disdainful weathermen, scorning the use of the word "hurricane", which by definition cannot happen in our latitudes, admitted that they were unable to give an accurate forecast. On Thursday 15th October, the computer in the Met. Office at Bracknell showed a moderate but deepening depression with a centre of 970 millibars just to the south of Cape Finisterre. The data and the lack of weatherships made it difficult to ascertain how fast it would deepen and which way it would go. There was no doubt that exceptionally strong winds would be coming across France, Belgium, Holland and The Channel but in Britain there was no such certainty.

Soon after midnight, the wind speed in Sussex was measured at 40mph and the centre of the low pressure area was near Bristol. Cold air plunging south over the Atlantic combined with warm air drawn from sub-tropical latitudes. On meeting, the depression was explosively deepened to produce a catastrophic force of turbulence and destructiveness.

The coastline from Selsey to Beachy Head was the first to suffer. Hardly a house, hotel or caravan, which over the years had trusted the goodwill of nature, was left undamaged. Peacehaven, standing on cliffs 100 feet above sea level, was devastated. Sun lounges collapsed in splinters, walls were sucked away, gable ends torn down and whole roofs lifted off and deposited somewhere to the north. Caravan sites stood no chance. At Rushy Hill, 200 people clad in pyjamas ran for their lives as the wind picked up their flimsy homes and then battered them beyond recognition.

At Hastings the gusting winds toppled a four-ton chimney at the Queen's Hotel sending it crashing through four storeys. Two guests somehow escaped injury as the chimney wiped out their rooms but Ronald Davies of Warwickshire was crushed beneath a mountain of bricks and mortar as he lay in bed. There was another tragedy at Hastings. "Boy ashore", Jimmy Read was hit by the roof of a winch hut as he helped drag up the fishermen's boats at the height of the storm. He lay undiscovered until a passer-by found him four hours later.

Sussex churches suffered badly. The spire of St Luke's United Reformed Church at St Leonards was lifted from its place and lowered intact into a side aisle of the church where a section of the roof had opened up to receive it. The 65 foot tall shingled spire of Rotherfield Parish Church collapsed in a tangle of twisted timbers. The Holy Cross Church of England School at Uckfield had the roofs ripped off

A four-ton chimney crashed through four floors of the Queen's Hotel, Hastings, killing a guest and opening a skyview.

six classrooms and the sports hall. The children spent three weeks away from lessons while new accommodation was found.

In Bexhill, a block of flats called The Marlowes was unroofed and more than 40 residents had to be evacuated. Two surgical wards at Bexhill Hospital had to be cleared of patients because cracks appeared in the walls. At South Cliff, Bexhill, Marjorie Doddington was preparing the house for her daughter's wedding reception in two days' time. There was a tremendous bang and the bedroom ceiling fell in. There was another bang and the whole roof was sucked away. It went over the house, over a hedge and landed in the street.

Further east in Brighton the whole town shook as if gripped by an earthquake. Elm trees in the grounds of Brighton Pavilion were thrown down and blue plastic sheeting which covered a section of the Pavilion under repair was torn to shreds. The scaffolding beneath was dislodged and struck the two-ton tip of one of the Pavilion's minarets which fell through the gilded dome of the Music Room and half buried itself in the floor. On top of the Downs above Brighton the famous windmills called Jack and Jill caught the wind and began to spin like the propeller of a helicopter. Jill caught fire and a massive tail of sparks lit up the hillside. Members of the preservation society were alerted. They crawled up the hill and were joined by more friends. In the

dead of night, in winds in excess of 100 mph, amid a deafening roar, a human chain was formed to pass buckets of water from a house 40 yards away to quell the flames. It took more than two hours.

In the parks and gardens the work of 400 years or more took four hours to destroy, or at least that is how it was seen in those bewildering hours after the storm. The Pleasure Ground at Petworth, lost trees planted by Capability Brown in the 1750's. They included the largest sweet chestnut ever recorded in Great Britain and a cedar of Lebanon of unrivalled splendour. At Sheffield Park in East Sussex, another of Capability's compositions, three giant Australian eucalyptus and a Monterey pine came down among others. At Nymans, they had 28 trees which were "champions" - the tallest or the largest in girth recorded of their kind. Only eight survived. Nymans also lost the largest Monkey Puzzle in the country. Wakehurst in the Weald, the Royal Botanical Gardens, lost 50 per cent of its important trees; Standen, near East Grinstead lost its famous mulberry and cedar and the celebrated beeches of Slindon Wood, near Arundel were cruelly mutilated.

Ashdown Forest which fans out over six thousand acres of heath, scrub and woodland was a natural target. In her book, *The Forest*, Barbara Willard describes the night. "Gathered birds were flung with panic, crying about the sky, lit by the perpetual livid flashing of pylons sagging and swaying under

A combination of hurricane-force winds and flooding brought heartbreak to Combe Haven Holiday Park, St Leonards.

the weight of fallen trees. The earth danced and spurted.....a burning salt-heavy atmosphere began to shrivel and destroy leaves already wilting......light came to show the Forest's face, twisted and distorted by this mightiest of strokes. No bright Autumn would spread over Ashdown now, for winter had already come." Between 300 and 500 of the Forest's 2,000 wooded acres were ravaged. Within weeks contractors were at the forefront in the battle to clear the mass of fallen timber and a replanting programme was initiated to assist the woodland's natural regeneration.

The hurricane-force wind bulldozed its relentless way across East and West Sussex. Selsey was completely cut off by fallen trees, light aeroplanes were turned on their backs at Shoreham and Goodwood, a massive British Rail crane was blown along the dock at Newhaven, rolled steel girders were bent in half like plasticine at Crawley and a set of aircraft steps was sent hurtling across the tarmac at Gatwick. Amidst this chaos there was time for grim humour typified by a police patrol car driver who called in from Hove to say he had just been overtaken by an unattended boat !

The days that followed the storm were not idle

ones. Electricity workers had the massive task of re-erecting the huge pylons and re-connecting miles and miles of overhead cables. Scores of linesmen from all over Britain were drafted in to augment the local work force. It took weeks of almost round-the-clock working and cost the life of a 20-year-old Welsh Electricity Board employee who was killed while working on overhead lines near Horsham.

There had been nothing to compare with the cost of the 1987 storm in Britain in modern times. As claims from private householders and businessmen started to flood in, the full enormity of that single night of fury began to emerge. Three weeks after the storm the Association of British Insurers estimated that claims had been coming in at the rate of 50,000 a day - and they were far from finished. The final compensation bill settled at around one and a half billion pounds. It was the biggest ever payout for damage caused by the weather and it was certainly the most catastrophic meteorological event that Sussex had ever experienced - and one that was unlikely to occur again for hundreds of years.

On 25th January, 1990, less than three years later, another storm of hurricane-force came ashore at Sussex.....

*Completely stoned ! A crashing flint wall wrecked parked cars in Southfields Road,
Eastbourne.*

Brighton's Royal Pavilion became a storm victim when the top of a minaret plunged through the ceiling of the Music Room, severely damaging a new carpet. Fifteen men took three hours to pull the globe out.

The Robert de Mortain public house on The Ridge at Hastings was badly damaged.

Below we see all that remained of one of Sussex's most famous landmarks, The Chanctonbury Ring, high on the South Downs above Worthing. The beech trees were planted in 1760 by 20-year-old Charles Goring, who also wrote a poem about the ring. At the time there was a public outcry by local people who feared the line of the South Downs would be ruined.

The Rushey Hill Caravan Park at Peacehaven where scores of people, clad only in their pyjamas, left their homes as they collapsed around them, and sought refuge in the village.

This aerial photograph of the Pebsham Valley, taken some days after the storm, shows many acres of marshland still flooded from the October rains.

Far from shipshape. A storm-tossed yacht at Bosham.

It was a "hurricane" at Shoreham

The great storm of October 16, 1987 was described as a "hurricane" by headline writers, by television and radio commentators and by everyone else in the affected area, apart from weathermen who, quite properly set a standard of precision for all climatic events. Hurricane is the name given to violent windstorms in the West Indies; they are a particular kind of tropical storm which cannot happen in latitudes like ours where the sea is never really warm enough to stir them up.

The October storm, however, was clearly related to the real thing, for it arrived on the tail of Hurricane Floyd, which itself caused a trail of devastation in the Caribbean.

According to the Beaufort scale, which is the criteria by which meteorologists measure the winds, Force 12 is listed as "hurricane" - and that has to be an average speed of 73 miles-an-hour or more, measured over ten minutes at a certain height above the ground. The weather station at Shoreham passed the ten-minute test with an average of 85 mph and a top speed of 115 mph. There, and in all the neighbouring communities, it certainly blew a "hurricane".

According to the Government, 15 million trees were lost and the National Trust estimated that it had lost nearly 8000 acres of woodland in the south-east. Appeals were quickly opened in every major town in East and West Sussex for the clearing and restoration. Children gave their pocket money, the elderly helped to sponsor the provision of new trees and families made donations of thousands of pounds.

Sussex certainly bore the brunt of the storm damage. For example, Chichester District Council's bill was in excess of £600,000 for the 1,500 homes affected. Altogether, local authorities in the south-east spent almost £100 million. The Ministry of Defence faced a bill of £15 million for repairs, British Rail, £1.5 million and Southern Water Authority, £2.25 million of which £1.5 million was covered by insurance.

An aerial view of Petworth Park, where sweet chestnuts, limes and planes, planted by Capability Brown in the 1750's, fell while in full leaf.

After the storm, and before the high whining song of the chain-saw, a strange, funereal calm descended on the Ashdown Forest. The people who knew the Forest well were united by grief and by the immensity of the great task that lay ahead.

It is possible that Blackwell Hollow in East Grinstead was the last road in England to be re-opened to traffic after the storm. This busy access route near to the town centre was impassable after huge trees, lining its banks, fell, causing many landslides. The banks were strengthened and more than a year later the road was finally opened to two-way traffic.

The branch line to Crawley ! - a scene repeated on every railway line right across Sussex. Further down the line there were a few hundred more.

When St Deny's Church at Rotherfield lost its famous spire in the storm - it rose 65 feet and was a familiar landmark for miles around - parishioners looked to the heavens for a new one. A reinforced concrete base was laid and a steel spire, constructed in Battle, was lowered into place by helicopter.

One of the most evocative photographs to be taken after the storm. It shows a lone figure walking through a totally wrecked zone, reminiscent of the aftermath of a great nuclear explosion. In the background, bringing a little comfort to the general scene, the evening lights of Hove shine in the gloom.

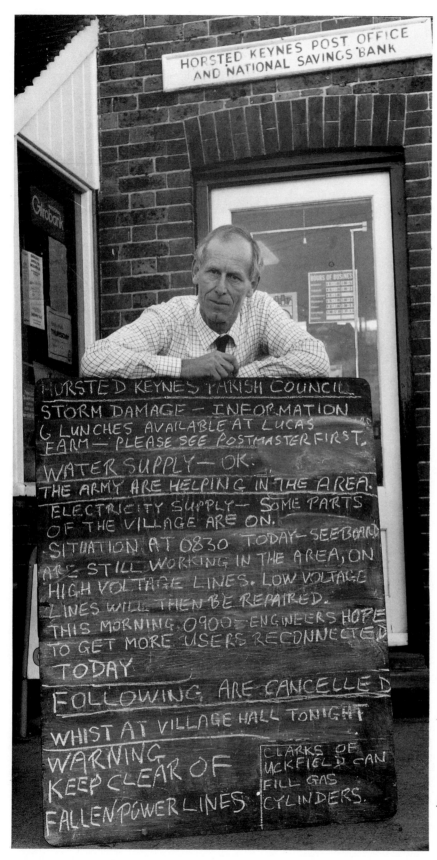

Most areas of Sussex were cut off from the outside world on the morning of 16th October, 1987. There was no telephone, no electricity and the roads were blocked with fallen trees. At Horsted Keynes, the village postmaster provided all the up-to-date information on a large board. It was certainly appreciated.

The morning after at the historic Old Steine, Brighton.

Paradise Road, Eastbourne. Following the storm it was far from heavenly.

This was a "family storm", for everyone was united by the shattering experience of fallen trees in the garden and the road outside. No task was too great as this family in Turners Hill Road, Worth are proving. Miraculously it happened at night. How would it have been if that roaring monster had attacked Sussex in the daytime ?

Peace in our time

One of the victims of the "hurricane" was Spike Milligan who was living in an Oasthouse in Ticehurst when the roof blew off. He and his wife spent an uncomfortable night in their car with the wind howling around them. We invited Spike to write his impressions of the night and this is what he had to say....

THEY'VE asked me to describe the hurricane, they must be mad, the hurricane lasted one million words! There I was, watching Michael Fish saying: "Don't worry, there is no hurricane", he was in direct line to Chamberlain's "peace in our time", so, as I sat eating my salmonella egg and my lysteria cheese, I knew there was peace in our time and no hurricane.

So that night, in my red night shirt, I drank my Horlicks and tucked into bed in an oasthouse in Ticehurst. Ah ! Late night on my portable TV, wait ! There's a strong whistling sound coming through the keyhole, never had that before, just stick a bit of cotton wool in, now what's wrong with this telly, the picture's all wobbly - it's one am, perhaps all the programmes have finished, blast the cotton wool's shot out of the keyhole again.

My wife, Shelagh comes in. "There's a very strong wind outside", she says, that's right, winds are always outside, that's where they belong, if the winds are inside then it's you. "But the wind is strong", she says. Yes, of course it's strong, weak winds haven't got any strength to get here. Now goodnight darling and put the cotton wool back.

Wife departs to her bedroom - she's shouting something about trees bent over. Now sleepy byes. Blast, why are those sheep lullabying so much, stupid things.....now the bloody cows, what's wrong with them - here, I say, was that a chicken that went past the window ? I mustn't put brandy in my Horlicks again.

Why have I woken up, what's the roaring noise ? Surely no lions in East Sussex ? What's the time ? Where's the bedside light?, blast the bulb's gone. Wow, there certainly is a wind, wasn't that another chicken past the window. God, there's a hell of a draught in the room - where's it coming from, try the room light, no, that bulb's gone, me torch ! Ah now, what the, there's a dazed pigeon on the floor, where'd he get in, shine the torch up. No. I am dreaming, the roof's gone.

My wife comes rushing in. "Spike, the end of the world is coming". That's it, 'phone the police ! 'phone's dead, another chicken past the window or was it a cow ? "The car", shouts the wife. "We've got to get into the car". She drags me out, that tree wasn't there before. Into the car then. "We'll be safe here", she says, as the car leans over at 60 degrees. Let's have the radio on. "This is the BBC Overseas Service, here is the news. Talks on the Middle East Hostages continued today....." We sleep fitfully, at dawn we survey the wreckage. "They must have dropped the bomb," says my wife tearfully.

The devastation at Nymans Gardens. After the storm Nymans entered a display made up of foliage from 40 different species of trees felled, and won a gold medal. Some described it as a "posthumous award". Within a year the gardens were restored to a new beauty.

The A259 coast road at Lancing was only open to cyclists and pedestrians on 15th December, 1989 after a combination of winds, heavy rain and high tide caused homes to be flooded and great damage to the seafront. It also aggravated an old controversy over a £1 million plan by Adur District Council to build 38 homes on a site that, many claimed, was notoriously close to ferocious seas.

CHAPTER TWELVE

The nineties hit the headlines

1990: A mild winter was offset by severe gales, the most damaging was on 25th January when, nationally, 47 people died — the greatest number of weather-related deaths since the east coast floods of 1953. February was exceptionally mild but early in the month there was a series of violent depressions with further gales of hurricane force. April was an exceptionally sunny month, a taste of things to come and, along the coast, July was the second sunniest of the century. In August the temperature at Herstmonceux exceeded 95F (35C). Hosepipe bans were imposed again and there were forest fires

1991: August was very dry with only 2mm of rain at Hastings. On 1st September temperatures reached 80F (26-27C) and it was the warmest day of the year. 13th November was an unsettled, thundery day and an inch of hail fell along the coast. From 28th November to 14th December (17 days) no rain fell in Brighton — a very rare seasonal drought.

1992: January was the driest since 1923 in-station record at Steyning with just 0.7 inch (17.5mm). Second driest winter since 1881 at Worthing. A very wet April with some localised flooding between 22nd and 30th with 4.3 ins (110mm) of rain at Steyning. A fabulous May with 300 hours of sun at Hove making it the warmest since 1877. Temperatures reached 81.5F (27.5C) at Birdham. On 20th July severe thunderstorms struck houses in Crawley and there was torrential rain in Hastings. Gusts of wind on 30th August reached 56mph and damage to roofs was reported in Burgess Hill. Severe hail and thunder on 20th October caused much damage at Burgess Hill and landslides on the A23 between Bolney and Handcross. Houses in Brighton were struck by lightning. In December, for the first time since 1990 the River Lavant was flowing.

1993: In February there was remarkably high average pressure leading to only 0.24 inch (6.1mm) of rain at Worthing. At Hove only 0.25 (6.3mm) of rain fell between 29th January and 20th March. September was wet and there were extensive power cuts around Chichester on the 7th. Several tornado funnel clouds were seen between Hurstpierpoint and Lewes on 11th September and again on 22nd near Lewes. There was a severe storm in Brighton on 11th October and an elderly lady was injured when struck by lightning at Woodingdean. There were mud slides on the Falmer to Rottingdean Road. December was the wettest in Brighton since 1934 with 7.24ins (185mm). There was severe flooding at the end of the month along the south coast. Burgess Hill recorded 431mm of rainfall from 7th September until the end of the year.

1994: Chichester was severely flooded from 4th to 10th January and there were landslides at Franklands Village near Haywards Heath. There was a snowstorm in parts of the county during the evening of 6th January. Deeper snow in mid-February, up to six inches in some places, caused the closure of 30 schools. The A22 at Forest Row was blocked for many hours when two lorries and a petrol tanker slithered to a halt on 15th but by the end of the day the snow had virtually all thawed. The winter was the wettest in the Brighton area since 1915/16. There were spectacular thunderstorms during the evening of 24th June throughout the county. July was very warm, in places the fifth warmest this century. The River Lavant was dry again. A very wet end to October with localised flooding at Burgess Hill. In spite of this rain it was a very sunny month and the autumn colours were glorious. November was most remarkable for being the warmest since records began in 1659; every day the temperature was above 50F(10C). Many plants were in flower and sea temperatures off Hastings reached 53F(11.6C) in December compared to the average of 46F(8C).

1995: January was the third wettest for two hundred years with flooding in many places, including the River Ouse from Isfield to Barcombe, the Arun, Adur and Cuckmere with Exceat and Alfriston on amber alert. In what was one of the most thundery winters on record Girl Guides were literally shaken out of their beds at Rustington Guide Centre on 21st January. A lamp post collapsed, a tree was badly damaged and a water main burst. Mud slides again blocked the Falmer Road at Rottingdean and there were over 100 emergency calls to the East Sussex Fire Brigade. In the Findon-Steyning area it was the wettest January since local records were initiated in the early 1920s. The winter was extremely mild, the eighth consecutive mild winter, making the longest run of mild winters since the middle of the 17th century. "As the days grow longer the cold grows stronger", an old Scandinavian proverb which came true in March as heavy snow fell on to wet ground and then froze; this was the first March snowfall for eight years. Trains ground to a halt on icy rails when points froze up in the Brighton and Eastbourne areas on the 9th. Ashdown Forest was covered in a thick mantle. Flash flooding on the 8th with rain pouring from the South Downs submerged places around Polegate with up to four feet of water. The following day Crawley was covered in a carpet of hail accompanied by a thunderstorm.

Churned up by hurricane-force winds, mountainous waves attacked the defences all along the Sussex coast on 25th January, 1990. It was only a brave man who risked standing on the promenade at Eastbourne, but photographer, Terence Connolly had a dangerous assignment.

Another tempest hits Sussex

25th January, 1990

"Was five and twenty days begun
'Twas thae a blast o' Janwar Win'
Blew hansel in on Robin."

Robert Burns - There was a lad.

ON the anniversary of the birth of the Scottish bard, Rabbie Burns, a storm centre passed over his old Ayrshire home. It was deeper than the October, 1987 tempest. Sussex was on its southern flank, where the wind speed reached 104 mph. With the working day in full swing the casualty list was high, 47 people losing their lives - six in Sussex.

The storm formed in a "jet stream", a band of fast flowing winds about six miles above the surface. On this occasion they were particularly powerful as contrasts between polar and tropical air over the Atlantic were very marked. The depression deepened rapidly, gathered its strength and headed towards Britain.

Two men died at Uppark House, Harting. Fire had ravaged the National Trust mansion and workmen were restoring the building, when the storm blew in. Site architects advised them to leave but, as they were packing up, part of a temporary roof was lifted off and fell onto the men below. Rescuers had to run for help as telephone lines had been severed, then emergency vehicles found the route to the house blocked with fallen trees. Three men died on the roads. A lorry was blown over on the A 259 at Guestling, killing the driver and another man died at Steyning when he fell from his moped. The third fatality was at Hailsham, where a tree fell across the path of a motorcyclist. At Gossops Green, a pensioner suffered a heart attack when a fence blew down on top of him.

It was a terrifying time for those working or living in tower blocks. At Newhaven, horrified pupils saw cracks appear in the walls of their three-storey high teaching unit. Teachers managed to evacuate them before the roof was ripped away. Beryl Westwood, a teacher at Pounds Hill, led her class to safety minutes before the building toppled like a pack of cards.

For the second time in three years hurricane force gusts ripped the roofing away from flats at Keymer Parade, near Burgess Hill. The debris crashed onto a busy street, trapping several people. They were not seriously injured. In Brighton two blocks of flats at Hollingbury, which had been extensively repaired after the 1987 storm, were again in danger of collapsing as many families fled to safety.

Even in the relative tranquility of the £5 million Swan Walk shopping centre at Horsham, plate glass fell 60 feet and just missed pasers by. Out to sea, 28 miles off Newhaven, 80 passengers and 50 crew on the cross-Channel ferry, *The Chartres,* were having a terrifying ordeal. In mountainous waves the steering failed and the ship wallowed for two hours before repairs were made. The captain made for Dieppe after ten hours at sea.

On land, power lines were sent crashing and the following morning more than 70,000 homes in Hastings, Rye, Tunbridge Wells and Crawley were without electricity. The chaos brought an ambulance dispute to a temporary halt as crews answered calls across the county. There were 200 casualties at Brighton's Royal Sussex County Hospital. Many people had been blown over in the wind.

At Selsey and the neighbouring Witterings, virtually every building sustained some damage. Villagers described the experienceas "more harrowing than 1987" The harbour master at Chichester described the storm as "very startling" but luckily there were less boats in the harbour than in the 1987 gale.

At Sidlesham and Almodington, one of the saddest sights was the destruction of thousands of pounds of crops as growers watched their greenhouses shatter before their own eyes. At First Avenue, Batchmere, near Chichester, Colwyn and Robbie Luck lost £3,000 of November-sown lettuce. With the storm approaching, they raced against time to harvest as many lettuces as possible. They were in the greenhouse when the first pane of glass shattered. They ran for cover and watched the greenhouse windows peel away like the skin of an orange.

Overall, the Burns Day storm was not as destructive as its infamous predecessor but in places, such as Patching and Arundel, damage was more severe. Further storms and heavy rain in early 1990 led to insurance claims that topped £2,500 million nationwide. Scientists claimed it was further proof that global warming was beginning to alter the climate.

The church at Ditchling took the full force of this tree which crashed in the storm of 25th January, 1990.

At the height of the storm, this tree fell onto a moving car at Patcham Mill on the London Road, Brighton.

Saltdean, near Brighton on 25th January, 1990. The salty spray from the whipped-up sea cascades onto a road which is some way from the sea.

The man who was staggering in the road and waving his arms at the traffic wasn't drunk. He was the bravest policeman in Brighton. Somehow, he managed to stay on his feet as winds approaching 100 mph blew around him on the afternoon of 25th January, 1990. This photograph, provided by TVS, is one of a famous sequence, which was seen by millions on the night of the storm.

The Worthing Inundation

26th February, 1990

THE great gale of January, 1990 faded into history but, in its wake, came a series of violent depressions which stormed in from the Atlantic and once again hit suffering Sussex below the belt. On 3rd February, the wind blew from Brighton to Dieppe at 100 mph in gusts and left 23 dead in France. More gales followed, but the one which the people of Worthing will always remember came on the night of Monday 26th February.

The storm began just three days after the southeast had enjoyed its warmest February day for years, with temperatures up to 64F (18C). It was accompanied by the highest tide of the year. It had already devastated the town of Towyn in Wales. It was to be called the Worthing Inundation.

The sea swept over Marine Parade and invaded the town centre as far as W.H.Smith. Several inches of water swirled through South Street and Montague Street, some 200 yards from the sea.

It all happened while most of Worthing slept, but Police Constable Glen Matthews, on duty at the time, rushed home, grabbed his camera and tripod, which he set up in South Street as the waves surged in. The enterprising policeman took this historic photograph at 1.30 am, during his tea break.

Worthing was not alone in its suffering. At Goring, the sea swept over the shingle bank and many homes were flooded. At Hastings, there was chaos on the seafront. Near Arundel, the fields were submerged.

The scene captured in Worthing by P.C. Glen Matthews and (inset) another view of South Street, flooded on New Year's Day, 1877.

Sussex wilts in the sunshine

Drought of 1989 - 1991

IN January, 1988, with the rain cascading down from leaden skies, with many places having between seven and eight inches (200mm) of rain and with Worthing experiencing its wettest January since 1880, no-one would have dared to predict that drought was to become a familiar word in the months ahead.

The weather steadily dried out. In Hove, there were 22 consecutive days without rain in June that year. The autumn and winter that followed provided insufficient rainfall to recharge the acquifers or boost the water table. Steyning received its lowest December rainfall since 1933 and January, 1989 was so mild and dry that daffodils were blooming in West Wittering by the middle of the month.

Then came May. No rain fell at Tunbridge Wells, and only 0.03 inches (less than a millimetre) at Crawley. The temperature topped 84F (29C). Water supplies were decreasing, particularly in Brighton and Worthing which depended on water borne from chalk strata. Inland, the situation was better with the Darwell Reservoir at Mountfield fairly full. After a cool, unsettled June, July was warm and dry and the thermometer soared to 88F, where it stayed for several days, touching 93F (34C) on the 22nd at Gatwick. Hosepipe bans were introduced for a quarter of a million people in the area around Brighton.

Summer, 1989 turned to autumn without the need for stand-pipes in the streets but the situation was worrying. However, a wild and wet winter was to follow with 16 inches (400mm) of rain, virtually no snow and a combined January and February temperature that was the warmest for more than 300 years. The weather pendulum swung again. Only 0.2 inches (2mm) of rain fell in March, 1990, generally considered to be the third warmest of the century. There was a heatwave in early May and, in July, the mercury soared to the upper 80's, the average daily sunshine reached 10 hours and water restrictions were back in the news.

Early August, 1990 brought the hottest weather ever measured in Britain with 99F (37.2C) at Cheltenham. Gatwick recorded 95F (35C) and passengers fainted while waiting for their aircraft. In Newhaven, the swing bridge expanded in the heat causing it to wedge in the open position, delaying hundreds of motorists. Firemen poured on hundreds of gallons of water to cool it down. A home mechanic nearly came to grief at Cowfold when the melting tar on the roadway caused his car to fall on top of him as he

was working underneath. Propping it up with his knees he shouted for help and neighbours managed to jack up the vehicle. There was a minor sensation at the Goodwood Races. Gentlemen in the Richmond enclosure were allowed to remove jackets !

Persistent high pressure which had caused the dry, sunny conditions was also responsible for chaos in the air waves as a sudden burst of French television appeared in the middle of East Enders. Reservoirs began to look like beaches at low tide, especially at Bewl Water, near Lamberhurst where huge stretches of sand became exposed. Everywhere in Sussex, the landscape was withered and brown and at Gatwick a pilot said it was like flying over Africa.

It was a hazardous time for firemen. A blaze swept through hundreds of acres of farmland and fields at Pound Hill, near Crawley and appliances from all over the county were rushed to the scene. There were numerous outbreaks of fire in the Ashdown Forest and in one blaze, several acres of rhododendron in the Buchan Country Park, south of Crawley, were destroyed.

On 4th August, Herstmonceux was the warmest place in Britain with 95F (35C) during the afternoon, a girl who ventured into the sea at Goring to cool off was stung by a Portugese Man-of-War jelly fish and the Crawley-based company who made fans had a million pounds worth of sales in what was to be a record-breaking week.

As cooler weather spread from Iceland, the great heatwave was over. Little rain accompanied the change and there were more heath and woodland fires. In October, however, there were thunderstorms. At Burgess Hill on 26th October, TV engineers were called out to 20 homes where aerial components had become welded by lightning.

By the end of the winter, in 1991, water companies were still not happy. Rivers were running at only half their normal flow and rain was desperately needed. An immediate crisis was averted by a wet June and July with 10 inches of rain along the coast. The summer rainfall, however, was ineffective due to evaporation and evapo-transpiration from trees and plants and when August provided virtually no rain at all - just 0.07 of an inch fell at Hastings - the clarion call to save water was introduced with even more vigour. As September began with the warmest day of the year and an absolute drought for the first two weeks, the call became louder and louder.

The great drought was not yet over.

Ardingly Reservoir on the 4th October, 1989 is reduced to a mere trickle as the great drought, destined to last for many more months, takes a grip on Sussex.

The wrong type of snow

February, 1991

FOR very young children, there was great excitement when heavy snow fell in February, 1991. It was the first real snow they had seen in Sussex. Parks and hillsides became huge adventure playgrounds as schools closed in the worst winter spell since January, 1987.

While the jubilant youngsters revelled in the deep snow, British Rail felt distinctly depressed. It was the wrong type of snow - the sort that is fine and blown off the ground into clouds. In fact, the sort that gets into the smallest crevices of a train engine and brings it to a halt. For three weeks, Network Southeast ran at half strength long after the snow melted. There was much damage to rolling stock.

The month got off to a cold start but the major freeze-up set in on the morning of Wednesday 6th February, when heavy snow showers gave a half-inch cover at Gatwick. By noon, the temperature at the airport had dropped to 27F (-3C) with an icy breeze blowing in the from east, By 3 pm a north-easterly was gusting cruelly, and a few hours later trains between London and Sussex were affected by a power failure at Three Bridges.

At midnight on 6th February, conditions deteriorated and the shipping forecast gave a remarkable warning of "light icing" on ships around Plymouth - an indication of the severity of the cold weather. By 7 am, the temperature had plunged to 12F (-11C). Radio Mercury opened its "snow-line service" and announced that scores of schools were closing across the region.

Thursday 7th February was one of the coldest days of this century. The "warmest" part of the day

TEMPERATURES ON 7TH FEBRUARY, 1991				
Place	Min F	(C)	Max F	(C)
Brighton	14	-10	23	-5
Bognor Regis	16	-9	23	-5
Eastbourne	18	-8	23	-5
Littlehamp'n	16	-9	25	-4
Hastings	16	-9	23	-5
Worthing	16	-9	25	-4
This day was one of the coldest this century				

at Littlehampton, Worthing and Shoreham, was 25F (-4C) - the same as in Moscow. This equalled the intense cold of February, 1956. The A259 at East Dean and the A27 between Firle and Polegate were impassable, as was the A26 at Boarshead. Villages near Robertsbridge were isolated. On this exceptionally cold day, the central heating failed in four tower blocks at St Leonards and 400 people were left shivering for hours.

An unexpected snowstorm on the night of Tuesday 12th February caused the worst conditions of the winter. Eight inches fell at Ore, five inches at Hailsham and four in Hastings. At the height of the storm, power cuts plunged the whole of Brighton and Hove into darkness. Cars were abandoned and some drivers slept in them all night.

A dramatic night was followed by a gentle thaw. Life in Sussex gradually got back to normal.

A snowplough at Turners Hill disturbs a pretty picture in February, 1991.

An Alpine town rests below the snow-capped mountainside as an intrepid skier steadies himself for the final descent. Wrong ! This is the downs above Hastings in February, 1991.

Thursday 7th February, 1991 was one of the coldest days of the century. This photograph taken from the groynes at Littlehampton, shows the giant icicles that had formed overnight.

Violent thunder and spectacular lightning, moving north over the Channel from France late in the evening of Friday 5th July, 1991, gave a dramatic display in the night sky over Sussex. The photograph was taken at Amberley Close, Littlehampton. A year later, on 21st July 1992, another severe storm hit Sussex and there was considerable damage to homes in Crawley.

Another October storm lashes Sussex

TORRENTIAL rain which swept northward along a line from Brighton to Lewes, Uckfield and Crowborough, caused vast damage in East Sussex on Monday 11th October 1993. The county fire brigade was overwhelmed with more than 100 emergency calls and a pensioner died on the road at the height of the storm.

Almost an inch of rain fell in 24 hours and disturbed again the ploughed fields above the village of Rottingdean. In a repetition of the great mudslide of 1987 a silt-laden torrent of mud, 220 yards long, burst from the hills and completely blocked the Falmer Road. Cars were stranded in the centre of Rottingdean as watery mud rose to a depth of two feet.

The pensioner who died was an 87-year-old pedestrian who was involved in a collison with a car in The Green, Rottingdean. Nearby at Woodingdean a woman was slightly injured when a bolt of lightning smashed through her lounge window.

Elizabeth Costello was watching television and could hear the storm outside. She told the Evening Argus that there was one almighty bang and lightning hit the window frame. "I felt my arm stinging and rushed upstairs because I was frightened. I then noticed there was blood on my arm". The bolt short-circuited video recorders and lights to several homes in the road.

The next day as East Sussex counted the cost of the flooding, police were advising drivers to avoid Rottingdean and Woodingdean.

In Lewes, which had suffered so much from flooding in the past, there was damage to the basement homes in Waterloo Place causing thousands of pounds of damage.

Weather experts said the October rainfall and subsequent flooding in East Sussex was the worst since the "hurricane" of 1987. Less than three months later Sussex -- east and west -- was experiencing the "greatest floods of the century".

'Waterless' Lavant returns to devastate Chichester

September 1993 - January 1994

FIVE years of below average rainfall by the end of 1992 had led to watercourses drying up and underground aquifers being at their lowest levels. One river, the Lavant, ran dry, its bed parched and cracked and almost forgotten by the residents of Chichester, who feared that the waterless river had disappeared for ever.

There is an old adage however which runs "No one so surely pays his debt, as wet to dry and dry to wet." Sure enough the rains came in earnest in September 1993 with 6.26 inches (160mm) in Chichester and a further 4.3 inches (108mm) during October. But it was December that brought almost incessant rain and then a small but very active area of low pressure moved along the Channel on 30th December and drenched the south of Sussex with 1.2 inches (29mm) in just two hours. As water was already pouring from flooded fields and meadows into watercourses, this proved to be the final straw that broke the camel's back.

All over Sussex rivers rose dramatically. At Uckfield the river Uck burst its banks, sending freezers and other such household items floating down the High Street. At Franklands Village, Haywards Heath, situated on a steep hillside, ominous cracks and splits in the ground more reminiscent of a devastating earthquake appeared and first one, then two properties had to be abandoned by tearful residents. Some 14 properties were eventually demolished as the rain-soaked sediments slumped downhill.

A red alert was issued by the National Rivers Authority. The Lavant returned with a vengeance, surging down its narrow man-made channel to burst its banks and send swirling floodwaters into the Hornet area, where it overwhelmed many shops and properties.

With vast amounts of water pouring in from the Downs a major rescue operation was mounted and firemen from all over the county were drafted in and worked day and night establishing a network of pipes and pumps. Ten vintage but efficient Green Goddess fire engines were brought out of mothballs to aid the rescue, a task that meant pumping 12 million gallons of water a day three miles into the sea at Fishbourne. The vehicles were soon surrounded by hay bales meant to deaden the noise but for days the drone of diesel pumps continually reverberated over the town centre.

Some families were evacuated and spent time at the West Gate Leisure Centre as 200,000 sandbags were sent to the town, many of them lining doorways and ground floor windows. One department store used polyurethane foam to seal the lower door frames. In some buildings water came in unexpectedly, forced up through cellars and flooring. All schools were shut for a time. A bulldozer piled a wall of earth along the Lavant behind the Hornet to contain the rushing waters. A team of Royal Navy divers sent an underwater camera into a 100-year-old culvert which ran under the area to see if it was about to collapse.

One of the most bizarre occurrences was when heavy rain suddenly turned to snow on the evening of Thursday 6th. As floodwaters swirled, everything above the water was covered in a beautiful filigree of snow with the backdrop of the Downs looking almost Alpine.

Out of town a massive military procedure to deal with the flooding swung into action. The course of part of the Lavant was altered at Westhampnett Mill which helped to alleviate the situation but it led to a rapid rise of water levels to the east and south of the town, swamping the old A27 and the A259. Windsurfers were seen on the ruffled waters of the A27, avoiding cars whose roofs protruded from what was now a huge lake. The army in the shape of the Royal Engineers from Maidstone and Aldershot were called in to help alleviate the traffic chaos and accepted the challenge to build two pontoon bridges, one of them 70 feet long and 14 feet wide and strong enough to take military tanks. Toiling long and hard under floodlights they erected steel structures which formed a ramp above the water. The task was completed and traffic flowed freely in the days ahead.

Upstream at Barnham and Singleton the RNLI were working on an inland sea rescuing marooned villagers. Further east at Storrington a tidal wave of water swept from the swollen River Stor through the High Street causing heartache and misery, none more so than at the Anchor Inn which had only just re-opened after a £100,000 refurbishment project. Within seconds the water burst in, ruining a £4,500 carpet, contorting and shattering new wood block flooring and overturning a giant fridge freezer which

The flooded streets of Singleton. Although living miles inland villagers in both Barnham and Singleton had to be rescued by lifeboatmen when they became marooned in their homes.

floated away from a back store room. Half the stock from the nearby Storrington Gallery floated out of the shop.

Nearby a large mill pond overflowed and confined a family in the Mill House to the first floor as a wave of water poured over the walls of the lake and rushed through a stable block, wrenching off two gate posts and pouring into the lower part of the dwelling through doors and windows. Firemen worked for several hours to shore up the banks of the lake with sandbags. The situation had an added sense of urgency as one of the occupants was mum-to-be Amanda, whose first child had been born prematurely. It was thought the anxiety of the situation might send her into labour, so the Solent Coast Guard helicopter stood by. Luckily it was not needed.

Five children and the driver were rescued by a man in a boat as their Landrover became submerged in floodwater in Chequer Lane, Bosham. They clambered out onto its roof and sang songs while they awaited rescue. Ironically, the man in the boat had himself driven into the same deep water, managed to scramble out of the vehicle and, after wading chest deep to the 'shore', found the dinghy with which he rescued the family.

The month continued to be unsettled with gale force winds, hail, further thunderstorms and spells of rain right up to the end. Lightning struck the City Flyer Express minutes after it took off from Gatwick Airport bound for Amsterdam and it had return to the airport where it made an emergency landing. By then the severe weather had cost West Sussex County Council alone, £1.9 million.

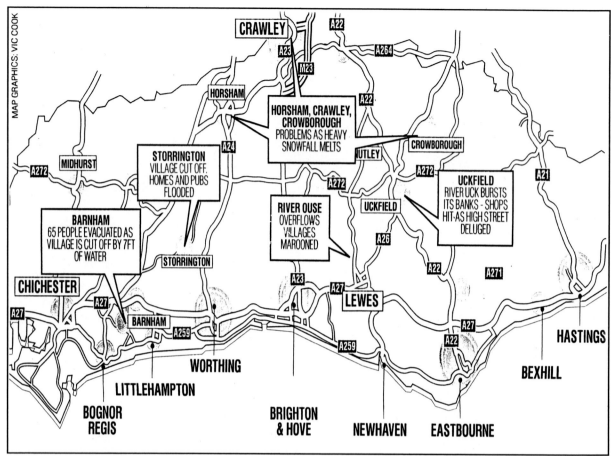

This is how the flooding affected Sussex in late December 1993 and January 1994. The graphic showing clearly the worst-hit areas was drawn by Vic Cook and published in a superb *Evening Argus* "Floods Special" on Friday 14th January, 1994. The county, which had been suffering from a prolonged drought just two years earlier, experienced the wettest December for almost 60 years. Rain lashed the south coast, producing 7.24ins (185mm) in four weeks. Here is a day-by-day build up to the deluge that was properly described as "the worst in living memory".

December 30th: Rain of tropical intensity. Hundreds of homes throughout Sussex are flooded.

December 31st: Floodwater surges into Uckfield High Street, tugging beer and food from the shops.

January 3rd: Rain-water fails to drain away in parts of Chichester. The Hornet, a busy road near the city centre, is closed to traffic.

January 4th: The River Lavant bursts its banks for the first time and many shops are flooded. Chichester District Council makes preparations to build a dam. Nearby homes are sandbagged.

January 5th: Several villages around Lewes are cut off as the River Ouse joins the River Uck and the River Lavant in bursting its confines to display some of its ancient power.

January 6th: Snow in January, not seen since 1987, adds to the chaos. Quite deep in Chichester, Crowborough, Arundel, Bognor, Crawley and Horsham.

January 7th: Water continues to rise. Ten Green Goddesses brought in to help fight floods in Chichester.

January 10th: The Lavant bursts its banks once more. Fire fighters pump water away from centre of city but main roads out of Chichester are blocked.

January 11th: The Army begins to build pontoon bridges over A27 and A259.

January 12th: Heavy rain returns and the Lavant reaches its highest level since 1852. Householders in Chichester are warned they may have to leave their homes and Brighton's new £60 million by-pass, opened a year previously, subsides.

January 13th: Floodwater races through Singleton to a depth of three feet. The village is cut off.

The incessant rains of December 1993 followed, just before the New Year by an active area of low pressure which drenched the county, proved too much for Franklands Village — a small community situated on a steep hill near Haywards Heath. The great soaking gave impetus to a year-old landslip and huge cracks began to appear in the ground. Fearful that the smart homes could slide off their promontory into the countryside below the authorities urged householders to abandon their doomed homes. Reluctantly and tearfully one family left followed by another. The land continued to slide, jagged edges appeared in the lawns, cracks in the walls of more houses and the decision was made to demolish them all. Eventually 14 houses on the 300-home estate were pulled down by the bulldozers in a scene that was more reminiscent of the second world war.

As a massive military operation went into action to deal with the floods, soldiers from the Royal Engineers were drafted in from Maidstone to plan bridge-building tactics across the blocked A27 and A259 from Bognor to Chichester. They set up their headquarters at County Hall, requested the help of the fire service and Territorial Army and then worked through the night under floodlights to build pontoons over the two main roads out of the city. The temporary bridge at Westhampnett, when completed, was 70 ft long and the second bridge at Merston, 50 ft long.

The following day, 12th January, Home Office minister Charles Wardle toured the city to assess damage to houses and shops and then crime prevention leaflets were sent to residents in case they had to leave their homes. But still the water was rising; in fact it was estimated that more than 1,500 million gallons of extra water went through Southern Water's pumping stations, storm drains and emergency overflows.

Photograph shows traffic flowing freely across the A259 at Merston. In the Hornet at Chichester, a temporary dam held back the swirling waters of the Lavant.

The 70 foot pontoon bridge spanning the A27 begins to take shape... At this stage the River Lavant was running at four times its average level and the flood on the old A27 at Chichester was five feet deep.

A freezer flows away along Uckfield High Street. The floodwater devastated a supermarket.

A windsurfer on the A27 is about to come to grief as he approaches an abandoned car. His friend continues in full sail! This was just one bizarre situation on the outskirts of Chichester in January 1994.

THE GREAT BATTLE CONTINUES

So, the great variety of weather for which Sussex is renowned goes on and on. There were more floods right across the two counties in January 1995 as the Rivers Ouse, Arun, Adur and Cuckmere burst their banks. Rottingdean suffered again from a mudslide and, in March, there was snow which brought trains to a halt and caused the usual traffic chaos. Despite this late cold snap the winter was mild and the spring kind. Meanwhile the never-ending struggle to improve sea defences continues along the most vulnerable areas on the Sussex coast as giant grabbers move in to haul vast rocks into place. Although they are proving more effective, this technique to hold back the sea is no more sophisticated than that adopted many centuries ago. The waves are still winning. Every year, somewhere on the stormy Sussex coast, a new hole is punched in the sea wall and engineers are constantly patching and replacing with such devices as pre-cast concrete wave return wall units. No-one, however, has ever dared to guarantee a defence against the sea. This is a battle which continues.

THE HIGHS AND THE LOWS OF SUSSEX

WARMEST MONTH

July, 1983 which enjoyed an average daily temperature of 68F (20C).

DRIEST PLACE

Icklesham was the driest place in Sussex with only 11.9 inches (304mm) in the whole of 1921.

SUNNIEST MONTH

The sunniest month was July, 1911 with 384 hours of sunshine at Hastings.

COLDEST MONTH

The coldest month in Sussex was January, 1963 with an average of just 28F (-2C).

WETTEST DAY

The wettest day was 10th October, 1980 at Durrington which received 5.25 inches (134mm).

WINDIEST DAY

The wind speed at Shoreham on 16th October, 1987 reached 115 miles an hour.

WETTEST PLACE

South Harting which received 57.31 inches (1464 mm) of rain in 1951.

SUNNIEST YEAR

The sunniest year was 1949 when Eastbourne enjoyed 2,153 hours of sunshine.

SNOWIEST MONTHS

Many inland areas had a snow cover from 26th December, 1962 to the 3rd March, 1963.

INDEX OF TOWNS, VILLAGES AND RIVERS

INDEX OF TOWNS, VILLAGES AND RIVERS

Bob Ogley

BOB was a journalist for 30 years until leaving the editorship of the *Sevenoaks Chronicle* in 1989 to become a full-time publisher and author. The overnight success of his first book *In The Wake of The Hurricane*, which became a national bestseller in both editions, launched him into publishing in the most dramatic way and he has since written a further six books. In 1990 he wrote *Biggin on The Bump*, the history of the RAF fighter station at Biggin Hill, which received tremendous reviews from national, local and aviation press. The book raised £15,000 in author's royalties for the RAF Benevolent Fund. His latest efforts, *Doodlebugs and Rockets* and *Kent at War* have been county bestsellers.

Bob has raised a further £60,000 with the hurricane books for environmental charities and has discovered a supplementary career as a speaker to clubs and organisations. Recently he has teamed up with Ian Currie and Mark Davison to write and publish the history of the weather in Kent, Essex, Norfolk and Suffolk, Hampshire and the Isle of Wight and Berkshire. *The Sussex Weather Book*, the seventh in this county weather series, has been updated and reprinted by popular demand.

Ian Currie

THE ever-changing moods and patterns in our weather have always fascinated Ian Currie. He has vivid child-hood memories of the 1958 thunderstorm and the deep winter snows of 1962-63, living then near Chislehurst in Kent. Sharing his interest with others has always been a feature of Ian's life. He writes a weekly weather column for several newspapers as well as being a weatherman for Radio Mercury and County Sound.

A graduate of Geography and Earth Science and teacher for 20 years, Ian is now a full-time writer and speaker to clubs and societies all over South-East England. He is a Fellow of the Royal Meteorological Society and a member of the Climatological Observers Link. Together with Mark Davison he has written *Surrey in The Hurricane, London's Hurricane, The Surrey Weather Book Red Sky at Night - Weather Sayings For All Seasons* and *Surrey in the Sixties*.

Mark Davison

MARK has been in local journalism for 15 years and is currently deputy editor of the *Surrey Mirror Series*. He is co-author of six county books on weather events and has shown a keen interest in the climate since the big freeze of 1962-3 when, as a small child, he was spell-bound by the heavy falls of snow. In January 1987 his interest was totally renewed.

Risking whatever the elements might try and throw at him, he has ventured out on many wild nights to gather first-hand accounts of the South East's storms and freezes. Together with Ian Currie he has produced a set of postcards commemorating the severe cold spell in February, 1991.

Froglets' Books

In The Wake of The Hurricane
(National Edition Reprint due Summer 1995)
ISBN 0 9513019 4 2.....................................£9.95

Surrey in The Hurricane
ISBN 0 9513019 2 6....................................£7.50

London's Hurricane
(Paperback) ISBN 0 9513019 3 4.................£4.95
(Hardback) ISBN 0 9513019 8 5...................£7.95

Eye on The Hurricane
(Eastern Counties)
(Paperback) ISBN 0 9513019 6 9.................£7.95
(Hardback) ISBN 0 9513019 7 7................£11.95

Biggin On The Bump (The most
famous fighter station in the world)
(Hardback) ISBN 1 872337 10 4 ....£16.99
(Paperback) ISBN 1 872337 05 8   ....£9.99

The Surrey Weather Book
Published by Frosted Earth
ISBN 0 9516710 1 4 ....£7.50

The Kent Weather Book
ISBN   1 872337 35 X £9.95

The Norfolk and Suffolk Weather Book
Paperback ISBN 1 872337 99 6...................£9.95
Hardback ISBN 1 872337 98 8...................£16.95

The Essex Weather Book
ISBN 1 872337 66 X £9.95

Hampshire and Isle of Wight Weather Book
ISBN 1 872337 20 1 ....£9.95

The Berkshire Weather Book
ISBN 1 872337 48 1.....................................£9.95

Doodlebugs and Rockets (The Battle
of the Flying Bombs)
(Hardback) ISBN 1 872337 22 8................£16.95
(Paperback) ISBN 1 872337 21 X..............£10.99

Kent at War
ISBN (paperback) 1 872337 82 1..............£10.99
ISBN (hardback) 1 872337 49 X..............£16.99

Flying Bombs over England (by H.E.Bates)
(Hardback) ISBN 1 872337 04 X...............£16.99